Guardians Of The Lamp

The Calgary General Hospital and its
Nursing School Remembered

Eleanor King Byers

*Remember Calgary's
"grand old girl"!
Eleanor King Byers*

Published in 2009 by Eleanor King Byers
1531 Varsity Estates Drive N.W.,
Calgary, Alberta, Canada T3B 3Y5
www.eleanorkingbyers.ca

Library and Archives Canada Cataloguing in Publication

King Byers, Eleanor, 1937-
Guardians of the lamp : the Calgary General Hospital
and its nursing school remembered / Eleanor King Byers.

Includes bibliographical references.
ISBN 978-0-9733420-1-7

1. Calgary General Hospital. School of Nursing--History.
2. Nursing--Study and teaching (Higher)--Alberta--Calgary--History.
I. Title.
RA983.C32 C35 2009   610.73'0711712338   C2009-901132-8

Editor: Rona Altrows
Layout/Design: Sherry Ward Design
Implosion photo (back cover): Calgary Herald with permission

Printed and bound in Canada
Second Printing

– FOREWORD –

Eleanor King Byers' second book will be of special interest to every Calgarian who was born at, who was a patient in, or who worked for the Calgary General Hospital. Equally, it will appeal to all those who simply admired the "grand old girl" that had been such an intrinsic part of Calgary's vigor — for one hundred and eight years. But *Guardians of the Lamp* will be especially treasured by everyone who ever graduated from the Calgary General Hospital School of Nursing.

Ms. Byers succinctly provides a history: of nursing, of "The Hospital," of the School of Nursing, and of her own time as a student nurse. But this is no dry history lesson. It is delivered with humor, affection and obvious respect for her profession, the institution and all the wonderful people who were part of her education.

Every CGH graduate will recognize scenes and people from her own student days, but there is also behind-the-scenes information many readers may not be familiar with. This is especially true where it relates to the politics behind the destruction of the physical plant and the tireless efforts to create new and better educational programs for nurses.

Byers skillfully chronicles many of the changes that have occurred in nursing and health care since the first cottage hospital in Calgary and the graduation of the first nurse in the province of Alberta, Marion Moodie, CGH, 1898. And, as in her first book, *The House With The Light On*, she provides us with updates for each chapter in the story. In the end, we are brought up to the present with a loving tribute to all CGH nurses and the organization which keeps the sisterhood together, the CGH Alumnae Association.

With honesty and insight, Eleanor King Byers has caught some of the magic that was part of the Calgary General Hospital, and she tells "our" story in a way that renews our sense of gratitude and pride in being a part of its history.

Catherine Smith (Munn, Class of '62),
President CGH Alumnae Association 2005/2006,
Daughter of Peggy Munn (Moodie, Class of '30),
Niece of Marion Moodie (Class of 1898) — first CGH graduate.

– DEDICATION –

To my sisters:

Vera Befus Baerg
Jessie Kasprow Balaski
Ruth Shepard Borgland
Patricia Miller Brearley
Evelyn Ginn Christensen
Allison Langford Christensen
Rene Zelenka Colombo
Patricia Olson Coptin
Joy Murray Crandall
Julia LaGrandeur Denis
Deanna Johnson Dutton
Shirley Ruttle Dyar
Joan Blewett Erickson
Sandra Falck
Carole Zoeteman Ferguson
Elaine Douglas Fisher
Fay Tomlinson Gathercole
Donna Gordon
Ann Greenfield Gorseth
Sandra Fraser Handy
Carol Smith Hardardt
Betty Lou Lovewell Hendrickson
Helen Fowler Heth
Edna Hill
Donalda Farris Hilton
Joyce Brown Hipkin
Mary Wright Hollifield
Irene Paulsen Inglis
Marjorie Ducommun Janzen
Arlone Jensen
Elaine Telford Karras
Carolyn Matthews Kelly
Doris Ratzlaff King
Edna Pitt Koloff
Andrea Mikkelsen Konschuh

Heather Dingwall Kraft
Beverly Cowles Larson
Irene Cwiklewich Lewis
Verna Tigner Lichlyter
Joanne Finch Little
Beatrice Handy Lyon
Mary McKenzie
Jean Collver McLennan
Marianna Middelberg
Faye Hustad Miklossy
Kinuyo Nishimura Minamide
Sheila Morgan
Lois Garland Nielsen
Elisabeth Jensen Parkkari
Darlene Miller Powell
Melinda Link Price
Wilma Jones Rad
Hedi Thiessen Ratzlaff
Lorraine Billings Ray
Edith McElheran Schroeder
Margaret Skarupa Skelton
Beverly Beers Smith
Elsie Groeneveld Steeves
Jean Kerry Strong
Myrna Wuest Strong
Lorraine Johnstone Sundvall
Patricia Swan
Sheila Bergwall Teghtmeyer
Sonja Olson Uglem
Laurie Doherty Watson
Eunice Smith Welsh
Donna Hamilton White
Joy Molyneux Whitehouse
Annie Wiens
Mildred Neufeld Wiens

"We have been banded together under pack codes and tribal laws."
— Rose Macaulay, on "Sisters"

In loving memory of our sisters who have gone ahead:

Doris Baerg
Dora Banister
Vera Rutschke Biko
Betty Burt Brown
Theola Stutz Dick
Glenora Erb
Winifred Frost
Juline Peterson Hande
Catherine Ward Heisen
Joanne Kell
Lorraine McCullagh
Audrey Muzyka
Valerie Erb Nicholson
Carol Thompson Purdy
Pearl Hammergren Rollman
Marion Johnson Spencer

...banded always

Photo: Courtesy Edith Schroeder

NURSE'S NOTES

Eleanor "Miss King" Byers

Throughout the book, the Calgary General Hospital will commonly be referred to as "the General," or by its familiar acronym, "CGH." It later became the Bow Valley Centre, "BVC," in conjunction with the Peter Lougheed Centre, "PLC."

I accept no responsibility for the accuracy of stories submitted to me by sisters who confess their own uncertainty about the exactitude of fifty-year-old tales resurrected by seventy-year-old brains. All stories, however, are rooted in reality, even if they appear to be a product of pure invention.

I refer to my sisters by last names only, a habit we adopted at the outset of our acquaintance, due to the absence of given names appearing in print form, and the school's practice of verbally addressing us with the formal salutation, "Miss King."

To the reader suddenly confronted with the realization that your life at one time lay precariously in the hands of one of the following frightened, fumbling — and occasionally, featherbrained — sisters learning on the job, your horror is justified. Hallelujah, you did survive.

Lastly, my apologies to the late Gertrude Hall for dashing your dream of shaping us all into poised *ladies*. If you could witness a Class of '59 reunion today, you would see how dismally you failed. What can I say, Miss Hall, except it was a lofty goal, and it was not our destiny. But if producing top drawer nurses was high on your list, then give yourself a pat on the back...

– A TRIBUTE TO OUR HOSPITAL –

It stands upon a rise of ground
Proudly viewing the city 'round,
For it belongs to people there,
As service is its cross to bear.
On one side casts its glances down
To view the southern side of town;
Then northward lifts its eager eyes
Where hills and houses line the skies.

Without a symbol of great strength
Withstanding cold of bitter length,
Within, a pulsing, living thing,
Where human hearts their burdens bring.

Heeds not that discrimination
Among peoples of its nation,
Its arms outstretched to any creed,
With willing hands to help their need.
And so it stands with peaceful grace,
With open heart and smiling face;
A stalwart form for us to see,
A symbol of our liberty.

— Lois Wakefield (Class of '55)

– CONTENTS –

– INTRODUCTION –

It was closed for more than a year prior to demolition.
It took twenty-three seconds to fall.
It took twenty minutes for the dust to settle.
It cost 9.5 million dollars to blow it up.

I am reminded of this reality each
time I step through the doorway
leading into my office, and nudge
the mortar-encrusted brick that
holds the door ajar. Mounted on
one side of this brick is a small
brass plaque reading *CALGARY
GENERAL HOSPITAL 1890 - 1998.*

A series of headlines surrounding the *Calgary General Hospital,*
my beloved alma mater, began appearing in *The Calgary Herald* in
1990, the first heralding its 100th anniversary celebration: "*Calgary
General* is 100"; "Hard-pressed Hundredth at CGH." Then came
warnings of unwelcome changes, beginning with its very name,
to *Bow Valley Centre,* and its battle for survival: "The *General
Hospital* On Life Support"; "Doctors, Nurses Fight To Keep Name";
"Acute Care Crisis." The culmination came with the final, crushing
notice of the hospital's proposed demolition: "*Bow Valley* Ends
Era"; "Last Rites For Dear Old Lady." I habitually clipped these
articles and tucked them into my CGH archive box, all the while
refusing to believe them. As the impending demise of my hospital
grew closer, I dug ever deeper into a state of denial... until the day
of reckoning dawned.

June 21, 1997 was a bit overcast, but comfortably warm, as I joined a large gathering of sympathizers — nurses, doctors and sentimentalists from every walk of life — in front of the *Calgary General Hospital* for a farewell ceremony. Each of us battled our own individual emotions as we stood reverently before the hospital's main entrance, but we were solidly united in our refusal to call this place *Bow Valley Centre*. As I huddled with a group of my classmates, a man standing at my elbow broke the silence of our mourning.

"I'll bet you were a nurse here," he said forlornly, sizing up my circle of friends.

"It's a good guess," I replied. "And your connection?"

"Oh," he answered, with a wistful half-smile, eyes glistening, "I was born here, that's all. But it seemed only right to come over and say good-bye." Suddenly, a stranger's words pushed me beyond my own narrow world — my selfish assumption that only those of us who had served this hospital, those who had tramped its halls through hectic days, unpredictable evenings, and lonely nights, could appreciate the loss. Now for the first time, I fully grasped the role this grand old institution played in the hearts and lives of thousands of Calgarians for over a century.

Following the ceremony, my classmates and I file inside to the cafeteria for one last tête-à-tête. As we sip glasses of lemonade, someone chortles, "I wonder how many gallons of this imperial juice we drank in our training days?"

"Imperial!" shriek the rest of us in unison, incredulous that we'd long forgotten the label for this sickly sweet, greenish-hued beverage now in hand, practically a staple throughout our student years. We raise our glasses to an *imperial* toast.

The day continues in this vein as we progress from the cafeteria through the familiar underground tunnel to our old residence. From the dim, damp corridor that snakes its way east from the hospital, a voice rises: "Remember screaming through here like a pack of banshees on the way to breakfast?"

"Especially on bacon days," comes a fast response. "Remember how the stingy cooks rationed servings to two slices?" We all have flashbacks to bacon days, when we shamelessly dumped one allotment onto the plate of another, plunked our now respectable four-slice serving onto our tray and pushed it toward the eggs.

"Such greed," I mumble, painfully aware of the number of times the bacon was entirely gone by the time I got to the cafeteria. I was a notoriously late riser.

"It wasn't greed," argues one defensive soul, seeking to ease her conscience. "It was hunger — interminable, insatiable, impossible hunger. I was ravenous for three solid years." It's evident I'm not about to send even one of my defiant companions on a guilt trip.

Then suddenly, we're there — the place that tugs at our heartstrings the most; the place where we spent three years laughing, crying, studying, playing, prankstering, sleeping, not sleeping, and baring our souls to one another; the place where we formed an abiding sisterhood — a sisterhood so indestructible it could thumb its nose at all the TNT a callous health authority could pack into its living quarters. We enter our beloved residence — our shared home.

All at once, the jesting stops. Thoughts of imperial juice and foaming-at-the-mouth banshees aren't as funny as they were five minutes ago. We're now wandering mute through a ramshackle wasteland of faintly familiar remnants from a bygone world, unaccountably scattered helter-skelter before us. We pass the blackboard-sized in/out board in the lobby, the workspace of our congenial switchboard operator, Mrs. Sanders. Her dust-ridden cramped cubicle is now barren of any hint of her. In a sentimental replay of a required ritual, I instinctively file by the board and flip the knob that announces to the residence ghosts that I am IN. Then a barely audible gasp breaks the silence: "Look at the sunken lounge!"

My mind races back to the September day forty-one years ago that I stepped, quivering, through the south doors, lugging my entire wardrobe in one suitcase. The first thing to greet me was this huge, lavish lounge with its parquet floor polished to such a dazzling shine it all but cried, "Don't walk on me." And reposing majestically at the far end of the room was the showpiece of the entire residence — a glistening grand piano. Magnificence beyond measure! Today the lounge lies in ruin. *I wonder where the piano went?*

Sunken Lounge and "the piano".

With heavy hearts, we shuffle our way through our crumbling home: to the classrooms, once lined with a long string of practice beds; downstairs to the pajama lounge, favored because it was the only common room in the place not demanding *proper* attire; back up to sneak a peek in the *beau* rooms, where we were ostensibly allowed to say goodnight to a beau in privacy behind closed doors, but if a kiss lasted longer than two seconds, you fully expected the door to fly open; and finally, through the seldom used, rather formal reading room leading to the elevators. We squeeze into an elevator and I press button number eight.

As we step off, we glance left down South Eight's hallway before turning our attention to North Eight, our old stomping ground. Both corridors, once a constant beehive of activity, now stand hauntingly lifeless. Room 801 — *my* room — is firmly barred. I can see through a crack in the door that it's empty. Chills creep up my spine as I realize the need for locking every last deserted room — an assurance that no one is inside when they light the fuse. As I peer through the crack, I long to be inside one more time, sitting cross-legged on my bed in my blue check dress, rapping with my buddies as they trickle in one by one returning from duty, discarding bibs and aprons as they chatter. *Oh, for just five minutes on my old bed!*

We have to content ourselves with a walkabout through the unsecured areas, and we poke our noses into the washrooms, the ironing room and down the laundry chute in our quest for reminders of good times. But our stroll down memory lane feels more like a mausoleum tour. We drag ourselves back to the elevator and retrace our steps to the outside world, the bustling world that is maddeningly oblivious to our approaching doom. I do not check myself OUT — no one cares. Wearily, we climb into our cars and ease from the curb, waving a final, sad farewell.

In the spring of 1998, a picture of a workman dismantling the *Bow Valley Centre* — the *Calgary General Hospital* to me — turned up in the newspaper. This was notice that doomsday was inching closer. I drove over to the site the next day and stood with my face pressed up against the fence, examining the work in progress. I spotted a pile of neatly stacked bricks alongside my old residence and waved down a nearby workman.

"Do you think I could have one of those bricks?" I ask, playing on his sympathies.

"My foreman has issued strict orders not to give away bricks," he replies curtly. "Apparently there's plans to raise funds by selling them in the fall."

"But I'll be on an extended trailer trip then. Just *one* brick?" I plead. He hesitates momentarily, and I pour on the charm. "Maybe if I talk to your foreman personally?" He whispers that his foreman has gone for lunch, then surreptitiously glances over his shoulder before tossing a brick over the fence. I scoop it up with a nod of thanks, and seal our conspiracy by swiftly slipping it into my shoulder bag, scurrying to my car and racing for home... where I tenderly place my new doorstop against my office door.

On October 4, 1998 the newspaper headlines changed: "The Big Boom"; "Fall Of The *General*." I was not home to read them, however. I was rolling along *Historic Route 66* with my husband, Dick. By sheer coincidence, my finger was tracing a New Mexico roadmap seeking the turnoff leading to the country residence of a nursing classmate. We were timing our visit with Joy and her husband Ken to take in Albuquerque's famous Balloon Festival. As the four of us watched the stunning array of balloons rise above the Sandia Mountains in blazing technicolor, Joy and I drifted past them to a faraway skyline — one that was colorless. A cloud of dust was falling over Calgary.

Calgary General Hospital implosion

Implosion photo: Calgary Herald with permission

Chapter 1

– OUR HISTORY –

An Unlikely Beginning

It all began in 1890 with the death of Jimmy Smith, an enthusiastic local citizen of Chinese descent, who had readily found a place in the hearts of Calgarians. Descriptions of Jimmy abound, each conflicting with the last:

> "He was an elderly Chinese immigrant." "He died in his twenties."

> "He died of tuberculosis in a room in the Royal Hotel." "He spent his final weeks in the home of Nelson and Lizzie Hoad."

> "He bequeathed personal items to select friends and the balance of his estate, in the amount of $600.00, to establish a fund to build a public hospital." "The balance of his estate was in the range of $1,200.00 to $2,000.00."

On it goes. However, we can be certain of a few facts: Jimmy Smith did exist; he died of tuberculosis at the age of twenty-six; and he did bequeath much of his estate to help fund a public hospital. Although the value of his estate varies with the teller, there is consensus that it was surprisingly sizeable, in view of his age, his education and his immigrant status. He was clearly an ambitious, hard working and frugal young man who wanted to make a difference.

To understand the driving force behind Jimmy Smith's exceptional bequest, we must step further back in Calgary's history to 1884, when Calgary was incorporated as a town. To serve its population of 500 people, it had two physicians, one dentist, two drugstores, a police force and a school. But no hospital. The

Canadian Pacific Railway had now chugged its way through the town on its its final leg west, delivering a rapid rise in population, and the city fathers began discussing the need for a medical facility. Not until 1886, when the situation was becoming increasingly urgent, did they form an official Hospital Committee to address the situation. The Committee was made up of members of the clergy, stalwarts of the business community and the town's three doctors, Doctors Henderson, Lindsay and Lafferty. The group succeeded in obtaining a 4 1/2 acre land grant north of the Bow River from the Territorial Government — a site familiar to present day Calgarians.

Yet unbelievably, all plans slipped into obscurity for another four years before interest was revived. During the same year that Jimmy died, a group of energetic, civic-minded women, headed by Mrs. Jean Pinkham, wife of the notable Bishop Cyprian Pinkham, rolled up their sleeves to join the cause initiated by their male counterparts on the Hospital Committee, formally establishing the Women's Hospital Aid Society (WHAS). It's reasonable to assume that Jimmy Smith, with his keen desire to play a role in the development of his adopted city, kept a watchful eye on the activities of these driving forces. Although Jimmy was a beloved friend to many civic leaders, he would have been all too aware that, because of his ethnicity, he might never be fully accepted into their inner circles. However, he knew of one certain way he could contribute to their cause. And so, Jimmy Smith drew up a will, which his lawyer friend, Sir James Lougheed, was honored to execute.

Did Jimmy die in the Royal Hotel or is that a legend that refuses to die? Frederick Hunter, a Calgary Historian, notes that no hotel of the time would have rented a room to any Chinese man of unknown means, never mind one suffering from a contagious disease. I'm inclined to agree with Mr. Hunter's belief that the Hoads, who included this personable young man amongst their circle of friends, took him into their care. Lizzie Hoad, Calgary's only trained nurse at the time, having received her training in Winnipeg, most assuredly nursed him through his final days. It's comforting to know that Jimmy Smith did not die alone, and in fact, he lives on in the hearts of every graduate of the Calgary General Hospital School of Nursing, the institution he helped launch.

Jimmy was one of the last citizens to be buried in the old cemetery at Shaganappi Point. Union Cemetery was opened that same year, and in time, all the Shaganappi graves, including Jimmy's, were moved to Union Cemetery. Unfortunately, Jimmy's gravestone rapidly deteriorated, and in 1922, the city's only option was to remove its crumbled remains. The grave lay unmarked for 80 years, until the Calgary General Hospital Nurses' Alumnae Association, in conjunction with its Museum and Historical Society, decided that Jimmy deserved better.

And so, on Tuesday, September 9, 2003, a group of alumnae members encircled Jimmy's grave site, and with heads bowed, dedicated a shiny new headstone in his honor. Until that day, our benefactor had always been a kind of mythical figure to most of us, but now, in a corner of Union Cemetery, Jimmy Smith came alive.

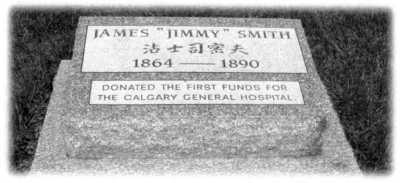

…in a corner of Union Cemetery, Jimmy Smith came alive.

Calgary General Hospital I
The "Cottage Hospital"
933 - 7th Avenue SW — November 24, 1890

At the same time that Jimmy Smith's bequest was gratefully received, the Hospital Fund was growing impressively through other sources, thanks to the tireless efforts of Mrs. Pinkham, who now pressed onward to the next stage. A charter was adopted, a board of directors elected and letters of incorporation were obtained. Temporary premises were procured in a two-story frame house at 933 - 7th Avenue SW, affectionately referred to as the "Cottage Hospital," which was rented for $35.00 per month. The home had originally been built for "Kitty" Evans, operator of a number of local brothels, and it was reputed to have "seen rougher days," as evidenced by bullet holes through some of the doors. I can imagine poor Mrs. Pinkham doing her best to ignore the possibly risqué history of her hard-won first Calgary General location.

The "Cottage Hospital," 1890

The "Cottage" had eight beds, four of which were on the main floor, along with an office, a kitchen and a dining room that doubled as an operating room when needed. The upstairs held four small "private" rooms for patients, plus two communal rooms shared by the rotating staff and the cook. Patients were treated for everything from the common cold and pneumonia to typhoid and alcoholism.

Elizabeth Hoad was appointed matron of the Cottage Hospital and her husband, Nelson Hoad took over nursing duties on the graveyard shift as well as handyman tasks as they cropped up. They drew a monumental combined income of $40.00 per month. A general assistant managed the cooking and laundry, while assisting Mrs. Hoad with nursing duties when time permitted. Amazingly, six doctors, each serving two-week rotations, formed the first medical staff: Doctors J. G. Calder, Henry George, Neville Lindsay, Harry Goodsir Mackid, Edward Rouleau and James Tofield. Dr. Mackid held the distinction of performing the first surgery... yes, in the dining room! It may have been a case of too many chiefs, because within six months, a mass resignation took place, reducing the medical team to Dr. Lindsay alone. In time, Dr. Mackid returned to the fold.

Meanwhile, Matron Hoad's first order of the day was to establish a means of controlling infection. Her protocol might best be described as "basic." She placed a basin of carbolic solution at the front door and issued orders for the medical staff to immerse their hands as they entered. (I break out in a rash at the very thought.)

Surgical requirements were next on the list, so Mrs. Hoad set about arranging the dining room in such a way that it could be converted into an operating theatre at a moment's notice. No doubt Mrs. Hoad could perform this marvel of stage management quickly, as the inventory of surgical instruments was sparse. Surgeons had no choice but to augment the meagre supply of gowns, sponges and instruments with their own personal stock.

The Calgary General Hospital's first Annual Report, issued

after only eight weeks of operation, revealed impressive figures in the black. Income from donations and patients' receipts totalled $1,882.00, while expenses (including the construction of a lean-to morgue) were held to $1,150.00. In celebration, the Hoads' salary was increased to $50.00 per month and a second nurse was added to the payroll.

In spite of the hospital's favorable financial status, however, it was readily apparent that its size was not meeting the needs of Calgary's mushrooming population. Yes, the first insufferable wait list was formed over a century ago! Yet for the next four years, the little cottage bravely struggled to serve the community, while Mrs. Pinkham and her Women's Hospital Aid Society directed all their energies toward the creation of a desperately needed larger facility. They forged ahead with endless fund-raising activities, salting away the proceeds from concerts, teas and sales a dollar at a time.

Then in 1894, Calgary was officially incorporated as a city, and to commemorate the occasion, the city fathers designated $10,000.00 of taxpayer money for a hospital — manna from heaven, when added to the sum raised by WHAS. The construction of a new hospital was inching closer to reality. Unfortunately, the site north of the Bow River, originally purchased for hospital use from the Territorial Government eight years prior, was deemed ineligible to receive contribution funds, since it did not fall within city limits. Once again, the search was on for suitable property, and without delay, twenty lots situated on 12th Avenue and 6th Street Southeast were acquired. Construction of Calgary General Hospital II began straightaway.

The "Cottage" returned to residential use for many years, then in 1963 it was demolished.

Calgary General Hospital II
12th Avenue and 6th Street SE — May 22, 1895

Many changes took place during the construction period leading up to the second hospital's opening. Matron Hoad resigned her position and Mary Ellen Birtles, who also hailed from Winnipeg, was hired as her replacement. Miss Birtles arrived in September, 1894 expecting to take up the reins of a gleaming new hospital. What a shock she must have gotten to discover construction had only just begun, and here she was in an understaffed, ill-equipped, crowded little house on Seventh Avenue.

Disappointment would lead to despair two days later, when her entire staff, such as it was, abandoned ship, leaving her with the entire line-up of housekeeping tasks in addition to nursing duties — around the clock. She did all that work for two months before another trained nurse came to her rescue.

Finally, Miss Birtles found a moment to address the concerns that had been plaguing her mind since her arrival: the potential demands of the new hospital. Having experienced first hand the rigors of 24-hour care for eight patients, she could foresee a desperate shortage of hands for a hospital with triple the bed count. Her solution was to develop a means of training her own staff. And so, the Calgary General Hospital School of Nursing was born... with a student population of <u>one</u>.

Miss Marion Moodie, the lone probationer, began her on-the-job training on April 23, 1895 with a solitary night shift — an assignment that included a long list of orders, which, considering her total lack of experience, must have been a formula for sheer terror.

Marion Moodie
1895

Those of us who followed Moodie's footsteps down through the decades are eternally in awe of this courageous young woman who forged our path.

Calgary General Hospital II, a handsome sandstone, finally opened on May 22, 1895. It was considered ultra modern with its electric lights, electric signal bells, dumbwaiter with communication tube connecting the main kitchen to the upper ward kitchen, and even a telephone in the matron's office. The spacious wards — five of them private — were heated by open-grated fireplaces, and an isolation ward was established with a separate staircase. The hospital's most extravagant item was an operating table imported from Montreal for the colossal sum of $117.22. And it did not sit in a dining room.

Calgary General Hospital II, 1895

Marion Moodie arrived at the new hospital as a student with one month's experience — a seasoned professional. Matron Birtles soon recruited seven additional helpmates to ease Moodie's workload while honing their own nursing skills in preparation for possible careers in the profession. A hospital ward had to be confiscated for their living quarters. As well, five doctors were added to the two-man medical staff of Doctors Lindsay and Mackid: Doctors Henrietta and Howard Denovan (husband and wife), George Macdonald, Andrew Porter and Robert Sanson. The hospital, now in full swing, not only drew the interest of local citizens, but frequently found itself the centre of attention.

Monetary donations, along with serviceable items, turned up with gratifying frequency. A. E. Cross, who some years later distinguished himself as one of the "Big Four" founders of the Calgary Stampede, is remembered as the donor of a crucial sterilizer for the operating room. (I hope that brought an end to the carbolic acid.) Other welcome additions were: free telephone service from Bell Telephone; a post office box, compliments of the postmaster, G. C. King; a light over the front door, installed by Calgary Power; and newspapers delivered by the local press. It was also not un-common for food, clothing, furniture or coal to appear unannounced. The hospital was clearly the pride and joy of Calgarians.

In no time, however, the pride and joy was filled to capacity, and hospital board members were once again putting their heads together to deal with a bed shortage. A separate maternity hospital and nurses' residence seemed to be the most practical immediate solution, so with full confidence that the dauntless Mrs. Pinkham and her trustworthy WHAS would raise the required funds, the board proceeded with construction plans forthwith. On September 12, 1899 — a mere four years after this hospital's launch — an adjacent maternity building opened its doors. Within six years, a much larger maternity ward was constructed, and the previous one was converted entirely into a nurses' residence.

On it went throughout the following years, the hospital constantly scrambling to deal with never-ending new demands and challenges. When sudden epidemics of communicable diseases, such as typhoid, diphtheria, scarlet fever or measles struck, the hospital's only means for handling the volume of patients in an isolated environment was to hastily pitch tents on the front lawn. Ultimately, a separate two-story isolation ward was erected in 1903 to manage this nightmare.

Maternity demands grew in leaps and bounds, as did the demands for student and graduate nurses. Finally, the day came when City Council had to acknowledge that their accustomed measure of adding to the existing hospital in response to overcrowding was no longer practical. A much larger facility was needed to address Calgary's phenomenal growth.

The summer of 1907 delivered the first event leading toward the prospect of a new hospital. The Honorable Frank Oliver, Minister of the Interior, granted an additional lot to the original territorial land grant of 1886 north of the Bow River, increasing the holding to seven and a half acres, which now fell within the borders of the ever-expanding city limits. The third site for the Calgary General Hospital was established. It would open in 1910, allowing the entire second site on Twelfth Avenue to operate solely as an isolation hospital for the next forty-four years... until the fourth and final Calgary General assumed responsibility for all communicable disease on its premises.

The Isolation Hospital was vacated and all patients were transferred across town in a move famously dubbed "Operation Measles." The dearly beloved Twelfth Avenue sandstone — scrubbed and painted — was adopted by the United Church as a seniors' home named Rundle Lodge. It operated as such from 1954 to 1971, when it had to be closed because of its decaying condition. When it was demolished in 1973, structure portions were retained on the grounds as a park scheme, and were dedicated as "Rundle Ruins" by Premier Peter Lougheed one year later. Today, the Rundle Ruins are the only physical remains of four Calgary General Hospitals over a one hundred and eight year history.

Rundle Ruins

Calgary General Hospital III
841 - Centre Avenue East — February 1, 1910

The official opening of the third Calgary General Hospital on February 1, 1910 was a joyous occasion chaired by the Lieutenant Governor, Dr. George Bulyea. Calgary's smart set, arriving in their finery for the celebration, had long given this event top priority on their social calendars. The ever faithful members of the Ladies' Aid Society considered it an honor to serve lunch.

The new hospital — which would come to be known as The "Red Brick" Hospital — was a five-story brick and sandstone building, with east and west wings reaching out from a main centre block. It had taken two years to build at a cost of 1.5 million dollars. Enthusiastic throngs gathered for the opening, and marvelled at

Photo: courtesy Jean McLennan

the expanse of the hospital, which now comfortably housed separate maternity and children's units, two operating rooms, four general wards and thirty-two private rooms, many of the latter generously furnished through donations from local citizens. The bed count had leapt to one hundred and sixty, so twenty-five student nurses had to be recruited immediately and many major changes had to be made to accommodate such a large scale operation. Within the first year, the Hospital Board wisely acquired enough additional land to increase their holdings to twenty acres. The unused land was landscaped into a park.

Calgary General Hospital III, 1910

The second hospital's primitive heating system had been freely maintained by any available staff members, but the high pressured boilers of this new, much larger building called for the expertise of qualified engineers to head up an official Maintenance Department. Similarly, a Laundry Department was required to operate the new, large power machines, which must have been a welcome upgrade from the previous method: boiling the bedding in lye, then doing washboard scrubbing and hand rinsing. Lastly, meal preparation graduated from two cooks managing the task — along with other duties — to a Diet Department of twenty who planned and prepared meals in the large fifth floor kitchen, and dispensed them by lift to the individual service pantries on each of the floors. The backbreaking task of hauling the coal to the main kitchen and pantry stoves theoretically belonged in the job description of the porter, but it frequently fell on the shoulders of one of the student nurses, who had no job description. Unimaginably, the Lady Superintendent oversaw the entire operation: maintenance, laundry and kitchen, as well as her entire nursing staff, which included directing the education of the nursing students.

Every ward echoed with empty beds in the spacious Calgary General III, and staff, agog with all this unfamiliar breathing room, naively surmised that the place would never fill to capacity. Within months they were eating their words. The calm, controlled atmosphere of the new hospital had erupted into chaos. The life-sustaining water of the Bow River had become contaminated with typhoid bacteria, and it spread like wildfire throughout the population.

Especially susceptible were the throngs of railway workers living in the construction camps that lined the riverbank. In no time, the hospital was bursting at the seams with these unfortunate victims; every last bed was occupied, and cots in the corridors were spilling onto the balconies. The mettle and versatility of the fledgling student nurses was put to the test early in the game, and by all accounts, they passed with first class honors. Dr. H. A. Gibson, a young doctor of the day, acknowledged, "They worked like slaves," adding with admiration, "I cannot remember a single complaint."

The city endured repeated typhoid outbreaks over the next few summers, and at peak times the hospital, once again, resorted to pitching tents on the lawn to manage the overwhelming caseload. There was a collective sigh of relief when a program to treat and bottle milk and chlorinate the water was finally implemented, effectively putting the lid on this annual nightmare.

In 1912, Calgary's first pathologist arrived to a buzz of excitement in the medical community. Dr. Rosamund Leacock (sister of the famed humorist, Stephen), fresh from the University of Toronto Medical School, took up positions on staff at both the Holy Cross and General Hospitals, while also maintaining a private laboratory on 17th Avenue and 4th Street West. All manner of activity took place in Dr. Leacock's lone assigned room at the General: she prepared her own testing materials, including the distillation of her own water supply; washed and sterilized all her own equipment; carried out requisitioned patient tests; performed purity tests on the city's water and milk supplies; and in the absence of a secretary, wrote up all her own reports.

Dr. Leacock was not the only doctor providing her own equipment. Throughout the early years, surgeons arrived at the operating room bearing their own instruments. Eventually, their meagre inventory was supplemented by hospital-owned instruments purchased through the generosity of a staff collection. One by one, further enhancements crept onto the scene: rubber gloves; the first x-ray machine (with a large, aggravatingly noisy motor); suction drainage; person-to-person blood transfusions; and an elevator that had a will of its own. When it refused to budge, patients were carried up and down the stairs on stretchers.

Around the onset of the First World War, an intern program was inaugurated and an official purchasing department and pharmacy were established. A full-time pharmacist, Miss A. Simpson, was eventually hired to deal with the inadequate practice of a local drugstore operating the hospital pharmacy during seriously limited hours. However, further progress slowed when nurses and doctors signed up in droves to serve overseas, creating a severe shortage on the home front. Remaining staff was largely made up of interns and student nurses, their twelve-hour shifts often stretching to sixteen hours, as the only means of managing the workload. One young graduate nurse, Miss Anne Hebert (Class of '13), was known to serve as night supervisor for a full six months without a day off. There was simply no one to relieve her. For a time, the enterprising hospital staff further came to the aid of the cause by managing both a vegetable garden and a poultry house on the premises to provide fresh vegetables and eggs for their patients.

The end of the war did not bring an end to the problems; the drain on staff continued as military medics followed the continued cry for help from military hospitals serving the injured veterans who now dotted the country. In spite of this dilemma, the Hospital Board could not ignore the harsh reality that the hospital still suffered a bed shortage. This was not a temporary situation — the result of an isolated typhoid outbreak — but rather a chronic, never-ending condition.

The Hospital Board addressed the question of whether to build a larger hospital, but deemed that move financially unfeasible at such a time, and so the solution was to build a separate nurses' residence. In February, 1919, exactly nine years after the hospital opened, "A" Block was built to house the nursing staff, and their vacated quarters in the main building provided the required space for patient beds. For a time, all was well. The hospital had enough beds and the nurses were provided for as never before with their own demonstration rooms, sitting rooms, laundry, kitchenette and storage room, all within their residence. Reportedly, the sitting rooms were furnished with eleven rocking chairs, but knowing the unending hours these women worked, I don't picture those rockers in motion very often.

Coinciding with the end of the war, a lethal "Spanish Flu" epidemic was circling the globe, and Calgary did not escape its fury. All infectious cases were admitted to the Isolation Hospital on the Twelfth Avenue premises of CGH II, but the need for additional staff at this location created a shortage at the main hospital. As the disease spread, makeshift hospitals were set up everywhere possible — in tents, at schools, in the Victoria Pavilion on the Stampede grounds. Women from every walk of life voluntarily stepped forward to assist with the nursing care of the flu victims. Still, throughout the demanding days of this scourge, hospital personnel never lost sight of their responsibility for the everyday medical needs of their community, both at the present time and into the future. This was also a period when nurses began looking to their own future, as they rallied for improvement in their own status.

In 1916 a "Registered Nurses Act" was passed, which officially recognized graduate nurses as professionals. By 1919, an amendment to the act placed the Alberta Association of Registered Nurses under the jurisdiction of the University of Alberta. A graduate nurse was now compelled to write standardized qualifying exams set by the university to earn the coveted initials "RN" after her name.

The twenties allowed a little breathing space to address such issues as the need for a "psychopathic" ward, although discussions led to an alarming solution: to bar the windows of one room on each medical floor in the hospital. It was a woeful concession that remained for the entire time that this building was in use. The idea of establishing small rural hospitals was also initiated at this time to relieve the demands on the larger centres, with a view to the large centres developing the worthwhile field of diagnostics for the entire population. Record keeping, non-existent or sporadic at best, became another issue requiring serious examination. Throughout the 1920s, a system of patient card indexing and charts slowly evolved until at long last a full-time stenographer was hired in 1937 to record histories and maintain records. This step paved the way to an eventual official Medical Records Department.

October 29, 1929 brought the infamous stock market crash that led to the desperate days of the "dirty thirties." The poor economy forced acute budget restrictions that included a relentless slash in salaries. Yet, the dire state-of-affairs was such that there was no shortage of nurses lined up for work on any pay scale. The nursing school was flooded with applicants from students, many doubtless pressured by despairing parents who viewed free room and board, plus an education for their daughters, as heaven-sent.

Not until the depression began lifting in the late 1930s could the Hospital Board turn its attention to two issues: the ongoing pressing need for more space and the obligation to improve on the hospital's embarrassing second-class rating, as pronounced by the American College of Surgeons. Now, however, the Second World War was brewing, dashing all hopes for an entirely new hospital.

Once again stopgap measures were implemented, the first by means of a new residence wing, known as "B" Block, opening in 1939, and west of it, a building designed for student lectures with an eight-bed practice ward. A noted impetus for the opening of these buildings was the increased student population that year, due to the addition of the psychiatric nursing students from Ponoka. In 1943, a third residence, "D" Block, was built and dubbed Sara MacDonald Hall in honor of a beloved Superintendent.

As the First World War had done, the Second World War created a shortage of registered nurses, pushing the Department of Veterans' Affairs to establish a school for nursing aides in 1946 to augment hospital staff. Initially, enrolment was restricted to armed forces personnel — ex-servicewomen who had experienced some medical training overseas — with classes held in quonset huts on the grounds of the Provincial Institute of Technology and Art, where SAIT is today. The forty-week program consisted of twenty weeks classroom instruction and twenty weeks clinical experience at the Calgary General and other provincial hospitals. By 1947, civilians were accepted as trainees, and the "Nursing Aides Act" was passed, providing official licensing for those successfully completing the standardized program. Nursing aides would become indispensable members of the medical team.

Nineteen forty-seven also witnessed a newly reorganized Ladies' Auxiliary to replace the Women's Hospital Aid Society. It would eventually become the Volunteer Services Department in 1962, assuming many functions, ranging from patient assistance and fund-raising, to the development of a "candy striper" program. Volunteers were invaluable to the Calgary General throughout its existence.

This was also a period when graduate nurses began to seriously examine the education of students, who, until then, were recruited primarily as low-cost labor and expected to perform a host of menial tasks as well as nursing duties. Two women whose names echoed through the halls long after they were gone, were Jessie Connal, Nursing Instructress from 1923 to 1949 and Sara MacDonald, Superintendent of Nurses from 1923 to 1941. Jessie Connal brought significant change to the education of her students by reorganizing and expanding the instruction program to cover each of the medical specialities. It was also under her tutelage that students from the

Alberta Mental Hospital in Ponoka first began two-year affiliations at the General and other city hospitals in 1939 to augment their psychiatric training.

On Sara MacDonald's death in 1941, Anne Hebert became Superintendent of Nurses. Miss Hebert served ten years before her resignation in 1951, when Margaret Macdonald took up the reins as Acting Superintendent until a permanent replacement could be found. These two committed women are also well remembered in the annals of the Calgary General's nursing history. Margaret Macdonald is best remembered as "Black Mac" the nickname she was given to distinguish her from Sara, the predecessor who shared the same surname. Sara's hair was white; Margaret's was black.

Prior to the war, a prominent Calgary couple, Eliza (a member of the first WHAS) and Henry (a hotelier) Perley, were taking an active interest in the General Hospital, and on Mr. Perley's death in 1934, a major portion of his estate was bequeathed to the hospital. With the city still struggling to rise from the depression, the decision was made to invest Mr. Perley's gift for use at a more stable time. The need for more space persisted, however, and by the 1940s the state of operating beyond capacity had become a fact of life. It was now determined that not even a world war justified further delay of expansion, and so the Henry Perley funds were activated. The Perley Wing opened in 1944, providing beds for three specialities: maternity (49 beds), pediatrics (26 cribs) and surgery (20 beds). Alas, in no time it was evident the fabulous new wing provided little more than a band-aid for a gaping wound.

It seems that very few patients or staff look back on the Red Brick Hospital with any degree of nostalgia. In 1936, Dr. G. Harvey Agnew, Executive Director of the Canadian Hospital Council, had appraised the hospital as, "... so badly designed that the only real solution is the erection of an entirely new plant, converting the present building into a home for incurables." Richard Needham, on describing the appalling layout of the hospital in a 1945 article in the *Calgary Herald*, wrote, "The building seems to have been erected by someone who had never seen a hospital, but had had one vaguely described to him." Some doctors maintained that the building was obsolete the day it opened. There was no reluctance to move forward with plans for Calgary General IV, which opened in 1953. The Red Brick variously housed nurses and interns for a brief period through the transition, along with doctors' offices and chronic care beds, before being demolished in 1959. In 1962 an eight-story Convalescent-Rehabilitation building was erected on its site.

Calgary General Hospital IV
841-Centre Avenue East — March 3, 1953

Opening ceremonies for the fourth Calgary General Hospital, the hospital familiar to my class, took place on March 3, 1953 with the Honorable J. J. Bowlen, Lieutenant-Governor of Alberta presiding. Two members from the school's alumnae were awarded deserving places of honor on the occasion: Miss Berta Van Gruenigin, the hospital's longest serving graduate, at 35 dedicated years, and Miss Marion Moodie, the school's first graduate. Miss Moodie was captivating in her high stiff collar and black boots, replicating the uniform she wore 50 years prior.

The new seven-floor building, designed for efficiency and comfort, brought the bed capacity up to 626 beds and 110 bassinets, more than doubling the previous bed count. It would open to the collective rejoicing of all involved. Breathing space at last. Yet scarcely a breath later, the administration was facing the imminent need for more beds, repeating the experience of the past three hospitals. The pattern is obviously a fact of life in the world of hospitals.

Within three years, two major additions were on the drawing board: a north wing to house radiology and administration in addition to medical wards; and a south wing pediatric unit. I remember both these additions rising from the dust during my student days. Still vivid is the exciting day in 1958 when I entered the gleaming new halls of North Six for the first time, inhaling the aroma of fresh paint as I rummaged about trying to find my bearings. I was in awe at the thought that people had undertaken the designing, constructing and then launching of such a place. My first bedpan assignment, however, revealed what I considered to be a design flaw in the floor plan. It made me think of my mother's complaint that kitchens were habitually designed by the gender who didn't do the cooking.

The service room was located a country mile from some of the wards. A nurse would have to cart the everlasting bedpan back and forth this distance, and the route took her indelicately through public domain — the front desk and the elevators — as she bore the unmistakable offering. In defense of sounding petty regarding an item that has reached near extinction today, I must remind the reader of two things regarding nursing in the 1950s: firstly, the bedpan was a routine, relentless essential, and secondly, the mindset of every nurse was to maintain a degree of dignity for her patients and for herself. That involved the judicious screening of all bodily discharges from public view, and to achieve that end, the nurse had to orchestrate her timing to avoid carrying bedpans past the flood of visitors who tumbled out of the elevators on the stroke of visiting hours.

Calgary General Hospital IV, 1953

From the beginning, the hospital's destiny was in the capable and dedicated hands of its Administrator, Dr. L. O. Bradley, whose burning desire was to transform the General from a lamentably outdated facility into a highly respected institution. From its inception, Dr. Bradley, a University of Alberta graduate, developed a master plan for the hospital's construction. It would have its own Isolation Ward (and the Isolation Hospital would then close); a new Laundry, which opened in July, 1954 operating at a capacity of 18 tons per week; a Psychiatric Ward fully equipped for drug, electro-stimuli and recreational therapy; and a completely renovated Perley Wing for maternity. That renovation was completed in January, 1955 (maternity having been temporarily housed in CGH III during construction). The plan also included refurbishing CGH III for chronic care use. Little wonder Dr. Bradley was described as a visionary.

Dr. Bradley also recognized that his goal could not be reached without the assistance of a highly trained nursing staff, and to that end, he recruited Gertrude May Hall, 1916 graduate of the Winnipeg Grace Hospital's one-year maternity program, 1921 graduate (gold medalist) of the Winnipeg General Hospital's regular three-year program. Miss Hall arrived with a wealth of knowledge. She had taken post graduate studies in teaching and supervision at McGill University, and this was followed by nursing experience on an international level. She served on the executive of numerous associations, holding positions such as CEO of the Manitoba Association of Registered Nurses and National Advisor and General Secretary of the Canadian Nurses' Association. She was renowned for her contribution to the World Health Organization, which she had served for many years on the Expert Committee on Nursing. In fact, she turned down WHO's offer for the position of Chief Nursing Officer to accept the Calgary General's Director of Nursing posting.

Gertrude Hall's overwhelming responsibilities included the redevelopment of a greatly enlarged nursing school; the establishment of new hospital services; and the preparation of staff from every sector of the hospital for work in their new environment. Sharing Dr. Bradley's vision for a first-rate hospital, she drew up her own master plan to achieve her goals. It began with co-ordinated meetings between nursing supervisors and heads of non-nursing departments to identify problems in areas in which they interacted. Then she turned her undivided attention to the area of nursing.

Her conviction that superior nursing care can only be achieved through teaching excellence, which in turn calls for higher education, led to her hiring choices. She brought in Margaret M. Street, a fellow graduate in teaching and supervision from McGill, as Associate Director of Nursing, and R. Catherine Aikin, fresh from post graduate studies at the University of Chicago, as Associate Director of Nursing Education. Miss Street had previously succeeded Miss Hall as CEO of the Manitoba Association of Registered Nurses, and had taught in hospitals across the country. Miss Aikin had acquired executive experience as assistant secretary-treasurer of the Association of Nurses of the Province of Quebec. We adored the soft, gentle Margaret Street and were terrified of the tough-as-nails Catherine Aikin.

Those three nurses were a major part of our entire student experience, but we missed out on getting to know Dr. Bradley, who moved on as we moved in, accepting the position as Administrator of the Winnipeg General Hospital. I did have a personal memory of Dr. Bradley, however, as a neighbor — the pleasant looking man I saw coming and going from his home directly across the street from my own. That happened during my carefree high school years when I had no grasp of the role this man was playing in the betterment of my city or the legacy he was leaving — one that would ultimately affect me personally. He left big shoes to fill, including the completion of his master plan, but Dr. J. Crosby Johnston, arriving directly from his position as Assistant Director of the University Hospital in Edmonton, stepped into those big shoes without breaking stride. Known for getting out from behind his desk to interact with staff, "Cob" Johnston was warmly embraced by the staff in return for the love and respect he showed them.

Dr. Johnston's first challenge of the fifties was to address the final stage of Dr. Bradley's master plan — the renovation of CGH III to be used for convalescent care. The proposal for this step was debated for two years, and it was finally decided that the 1910 building was beyond retrieval. It was razed in 1959 to make way for an entirely new convalescent/rehabilitation facility. The eight-story facility opened in 1962 under the direction of Dr. David Blair. The opening reflected Dr. Johnston's philosophy that treating a patient's illness was not enough; the patient had to be equipped to cope with the effects of the illness in the outside world. Until now, this grey area between sickness and health had largely been neglected. Rehabilitation — including physical, occupational and speech therapists; psychologists and social workers; as well as doctors and nurses — had now become an important and honored speciality unto itself.

Through the years, the hospital was constantly reinventing itself to accommodate the rapid changes in medicine and the growth of the city. It maintained a seemingly permanent posture of planning, changing, adding, renovating, razing. In 1955, a comprehensive diabetic service was instituted, co-ordinating medical, nursing and dietetic staffs, while providing the all-important patient education. It was the first community hospital in Canada to embrace such a service. However, Calgary lagged far behind the rest of the country in another field.

Mental illness was treated almost exclusively in the two large provincial institutions in Ponoka and Oliver, while local medical wards isolated a small number of beds for treating mild cases as they presented. Dr. Morris Carnat, a local pioneer in the field, and the first certified psychiatrist in Calgary, continued to describe the city's approach to psychiatric services as medieval. Eventually, the General opened an independent Psychiatric Ward in 1954, although too often, the ward's main role was to diagnose and refer patients to the larger institutions. Dr. Jules Lamarre, a director of the department of psychiatry, made an interesting statement that holds astonishing relevance today: "The problems that create psychological dysfunction are present in Calgary to a greater degree than in most Canadian communities. With its extraordinary rate of expansion, an accompanying degree of social instability has been created. We get a lot of transient people with no support system."

Meanwhile, Dr. D. K. Lander, a Black Diamond psychiatrist, was endeavoring to bring psychiatry out of the dark ages his way, namely by fostering its role in aiding the effectiveness of conventional treatments for general medical conditions. The *Calgary Herald*, Saturday, May 25, 1957, offered a quote from his speech at an AARN meeting, in which he cited ulcers as a prime example of his inimitable philosophy: "Ulcers are due one-third to diet and two-thirds to home life, and it's not what you eat, but what's eating you. Many an executive's ulcer can be traced to the cold shoulder and hot tongue of his wife." His theory, which traced the cause of gastric ulcers to a patient's lifestyle, was a common belief at the time. He might well have risked dismissal of this theory, however, by linking it with his apparent prejudice of women. I'm also shocked at his lack of wisdom in exposing such a bias before an all-female audience. Ultimately, the long-held notion linking ulcers to lifestyle, was debunked. Today, we recognize the cause to be bacterial infection — a circumstance that is successfully treated with antibiotics.

In 1958, the Emergency Ward was revised and expanded to include a Poison Information Centre, and a Disaster Program was established. That same year, the introduction of the Alberta Hospitalization Plan brought significant changes to health care, with the federal and provincial governments sharing the cost burden with tax funds. A Dental Operating Room, reputed to be the only one of its kind in Canada, was the General's final addition in the fifties.

The 1960s brought the introduction of Chaplaincy Services; Speech, Occupational and Recreation Therapies; Respiratory Technology, resulting in a two-year program in Inhalation Therapy (later moved to SAIT); Home Services, including the Victorian

Order of Nurses; and Prosthetics. But the sixties, also brought great turmoil.

By 1960, the city had 4.5 beds per 1,000 residents, far below the provincial average of 7.5 beds. The waiting list had become a chronic news item in the local paper, and facilities and staff were stretched to the limit. Gertrude Hall and Dr. Johnston feared the effects this state of affairs would have on staff morale and the safety of patients. Needless to say, they were aghast when their request for increased funding was rejected by City Council, and the outspoken mayor, Harry Hayes, accused the hospital of top-heavy administration and frivolous spending not essential to patient care. He proposed a budget cut of $100,000.00.

Though bristling at the accusations, Dr. Johnston composed a non-inflammatory letter to Council requesting practical suggestions for areas in which costs might be effectively reduced. Unfortunately, the letter incensed the narrow-minded aldermen who now dug in their heels. Among many advocates, Dr. Johnston found a strong sympathizer in the editor of *The Albertan*, who deemed his request reasonable, and suggested that "outbursts of peevish temper are a poor substitute for a well reasoned answer. Obviously Dr. Johnston is convinced that reducing hospital costs is going to reduce hospital standards. Harsh words won't solve the problem." His words fell on deaf ears.

Dr. Johnston made a gallant effort to defuse the controversy, launching a study to explore the best areas to implement cuts with the least damage to the efficiency of the hospital. Shaving costs from every possible nook and cranny, he could only reduce the budget by half the amount demanded by Council. Gertrude Hall, foreseeing a decline in the quality of care in the hospital she had worked tirelessly to raise from mediocrity to her lofty standards, handed in her resignation. Margaret Street followed suit the next day.

Miss Street packed to leave for Boston to further her studies in a nursing administration masters degree program. Miss Hall accepted a three-year contract with the Toronto Sick Children's Hospital to direct a survey project. She did not fulfil that contract. On October 14, 1960, a cardiac arrest took her on the stage of the school auditorium, in the fading moments of the graduation ceremonies for her last class — a shocking close to a brief but powerful tenure at the Calgary General Hospital. She was just 63 years old.

Her death delivered a crushing blow to many, most of all to Crosby Johnston, who summed up his sentiments in describing her as a modern day Florence Nightingale: "Her life was a dedication to two traits of human greatness — compassion for the ill and thorough teaching for those in her profession." He added that, "she was aggrieved of heart when something less than the best had to be done." One might suggest she died of an aggrieved heart.

Within the same decade, a major change in the administrative structure of the hospital also took place. The Board eliminated the overall position of Administrator, replacing it with two coequal positions: Executive Director Medical, a position retained by Dr. Johnston; and Executive Director Administration, a post held by Mr. Menzies M. Dyck. Throughout all the changes, Gertrude Hall's memory remained constant. Her spirit walked the halls to the end.

By the late 1960s, City Council could not turn its back on the results of a 3-year study of the hospital's entire physical plant, which determined that a number of areas were cramped, inadequately equipped, and out of date — everything from business and staff offices to surgical suites, pharmacy, central supply, and emergency. A major Service Wing was erected south of the main hospital to address the problem by rehousing these major operational facilities into larger, more efficient work spaces. The addition did not increase the bed count, but it did pave the way for the rest of the hospital to be reorganized and refurbished, improving conditions for both patients and staff. Having survived the turmoil of the early sixties and the success of the late sixties, the hospital's tireless Medical Director now set his sights on a long-held dream.

Dr. Johnston moved into the new decade with optimism and enthusiasm by advancing his unceasing belief that family practice is the cornerstone of a community's health. Recognizing that the family physician was becoming an endangered species in the present day world of specialization and exploding technology, he established a Family Medicine training program in conjunction with the University of Calgary Faculty of Medicine. The three-year residency program, designed to equip the intern with the complex set of skills required for the vital role of family practitioner, was the first of its kind west of Toronto. The Gertrude M. Hall Education Wing, erected north of the main building in 1970, was designed to accommodate the program.

While all this was materializing, deliberations in the field of Psychiatry were simmering in the background. The dismal psychiatric ward in the hospital's basement had become obsolete. In 1969, Dr. W. R. N. Blair, chair of the Psychology Department of the University of Calgary, directed a study of mental health programs in the province that set in motion sweeping changes in mental health care. A new wing was proposed for the General to accommodate psychiatric facilities. It had scarcely reached the drawing board when the move to reduce admissions to Ponoka and Oliver began.

Endless discussions revolved around the proposed psychiatric wing, with cost estimates rising with every modification in plans, beginning with $13.9 million for 9 stories, then creeping up to $18 million and 10 stories. As with every preceding addition to the hospital, this one would create a domino effect.

The Perley Wing, housing Obstetrics, was deemed to be the most suitable site for the Psychiatric addition, except that its structure was judged too unstable to accommodate an addition of the intended size. And so, it was down with the old and up with the new: two stories were added to the new Service Wing for Obstetrics; the Perley Wing was razed; and the new ten-story Centennial Wing, later officially named The Carnat Centre, was erected in its place. In addition to its 75 Psychiatric beds, a groundbreaking Forensic unit of 46 beds was established in conjunction — a first in Canada. Room was also made for a 31-bed Intensive Care Unit, a cafeteria and a library. The 1977 opening of the spectacular Centennial Wing set the city abuzz with pride. It would be the last medical addition to the Calgary General Hospital. It lived a mere 21 years before crumbling.

In 1983, a massive Calgary Hospitals Regional Laundry was erected just south of the residence. In addition to serving the General, its sophisticated, cost-effective technology provided centralized laundry service for 3,000 beds at eleven hospitals and nursing homes across the city. It escaped the implosion. But in the spring of 2008, it was demolished to clear the land for the final phase of the area's condo development. It had lived to the ripe old age of twenty-five.

When I replay videotape today of the hospital's implosion, my eye is drawn upward to the majestic smoke stack that had marked the location of the old laundry familiar to me. On a clear, crisp October morning, the stack — piercing the sky in proud defiance — is a sight to behold. I still hold my breath as I watch it fight for survival; I pull for it to "hang on" as it teeters on the brink, bravely clinging to life after every surrounding building has collapsed at its feet. But alas, it gives up the ghost.

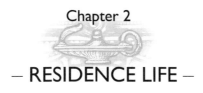

Chapter 2

— RESIDENCE LIFE —

Settling In

On May 12, 1956 the dazzling new residence threw open its doors to three classes of stampeding student nurses who'd been anxiously watching and waiting for this day from their meagre quarters in "B" Block or "D" Block down the way, or the silverfish-infested old Brick Hospital next door. (Was it a coincidence that May 12 was the birthday of Florence Nightingale?) As the girls unpacked in individual rooms for the first time, they could scarcely believe their good fortune. The Class of '56 would not live in this residence long enough to look back on it as home, but they nevertheless weren't sneezing at a decided upgrade of accommodation for their final four months. The Class of '57 lived there for their senior year only, the Class of '58 for their intermediate and senior years, and we in the Class of '59 were the first to luxuriate in the glamorous new surroundings for our entire three years. Impeccable timing!

Calgary General Hospital IV — Nurse's Residence, 1956

One hundred fifteen of us arrived on Tuesday, September 4, 1956, many of us dragging our entire worldly possessions in one or two pieces of luggage. We had packed the critical items first — those listed on a letter of instructions we'd received well in advance of this day: a watch with a second hand; an alarm clock; a fountain pen — one that holds ink — students may <u>not</u> carry ink bottles around with them; a loose-leaf notebook; a white cardigan sweater; white hosiery; tailored, white, washable slips and lingerie; adequate foundation garments; a bag for soiled clothes; other personal clothing — be sure to include a dressing gown. As an addition to the list, we were cautioned, "you are earnestly requested to refrain from bringing with you valuable jewellery or an amount of money in excess of reasonable requirements." This request did not put me in a quandary.

As we stepped through the doors into a foreign world, we had no idea what was in store for us, but we were fairly certain that, whatever it was, our life experience thus far had not armed us. Glistening eyes betrayed our stab at bravery as we bade farewell to those who had delivered us to our fate: parents, siblings, girlfriends, boyfriends. Many of us felt the pangs of homesickness before their cars had faded from sight below the crest of the hill. We Calgary girls had the advantage of at least knowing the ins and outs of city life, as well as having the security of our families at arm's length, but for those arriving from small towns or farms — and there were many — the adjustment must have been overwhelming.

Zelenka, arriving in the *big city* from a farm in Taber, circled her room in disbelief. The farmhouse she had left behind had no running water, an outhouse, and an oil furnace in the floor between the kitchen and the living room that fell short of warming the bedrooms. Winter mornings began with a chorus of six sisters sucking their breath as they slid from their beds onto icy cold floors.

Yet the physical comfort of her new surroundings did nothing to ease Zelenka's feeling of desolation as she closed her door and slumped into the lone chair by the window. *Should I just hide in here for the rest of the day?* She was tempted. *No, better not. I might start crying and I'll never get stopped.* She mustered the courage — backed by curiosity — to open her door and sidle down the hall in search of a friendly face. She found one just a few doors away. "Hi, I'm Morgan. Do you know anyone around here or are you alone, too?" Morgan reminded her of a friendly puppy, and she was amazed that things looked brighter already.

The next morning, as Zelenka stepped onto the elevator to attend compulsory chapel, she met a second friend. "Hold the elevator! I'm coming!" It was the somewhat aloof girl she'd seen in the room across the hall, the one she would definitely not describe as a "friendly puppy." Miss Aloof flew onto the elevator, fumbling with undone buttons as she stumbled over her untied shoes. Little did the early rising farm girl know this would be her destiny for the next three years: holding the elevator for the nocturnal city slicker across the hall — the one who now, and habitually ever after, performed her finishing touches on board.

The ride down that first day produced a welcome revelation for Zelenka — that she had confused aloofness with shyness. That was nothing a robust four-floor laugh wouldn't cure. And so, by the time the elevator had delivered these two girls to their main floor destination, their contrasting worlds had evaporated, and an easy friendship was born. They were strangers getting on, buddies getting off. Buddies for life. Incidentally, the city girl's name was King.

McElheran and Zelenka both still speak of the excitement they felt in having a room of their own, since they had come from a lifetime of sharing quarters with sisters. For the first time in their lives they experienced having *their* room, *their* way — their idea of heaven. Still, there was a sense of loss as they adjusted to unfamiliar emptiness: no whispered giggles in the dark; no good night voice when they clicked off their light; no sleepy-eyed face squinting from the next pillow when the sun came up. Yet, in other rooms, next door or across the hall, those of us accustomed to a room of our own calmly unpacked with the selfish assumption that this was our due.

L. Jensen paints a graphic picture of growing up on a dairy farm near Cochrane, the youngest of six. The small family farmhouse had no electricity, no gas, no water, no telephone. She rode her horse to a one-room schoolhouse for grades one to nine, and then it was off to boarding school at Camrose Lutheran College for high school. On graduation, Jensen faced the same decision confronting all youths her age: what next? She saw no future in returning to the farm, so she began to entertain the idea of nursing school. The more she thought about it, the more appealing it became: free room and board; free education; free uniforms; and even though she'd have to move to the city, which in her mind meant ugly brick and cement, at least she wouldn't have to wear the high-heeled shoes she'd observed on the streets during family excursions to town. She called them silly city shoes. As for dorm life, her three years at boarding school would give her the leg up over the other girls.

And so, fresh-faced and full of enthusiasm, Jensen breezed into the nurse's residence... where she was thunderstruck by the vision before her. *This isn't a dorm*, she gasped under her breath, *this is Buckingham Palace!* She froze in her tracks, eyes riveted to the grand sunken lounge, until someone broke the spell with an offer to deliver her to her room, where a second surprise awaited her. "You mean I get a room all to myself?" she shrieked. "I've never had a room of my own. And look, it has a sink!" She was tipsy with the heady thrill of her extravagant new surroundings, turning round and round as she grappled to take it all in. Then suddenly, and radically, her mood changed. She was experiencing loneliness as never before. *If only I could phone home*, she agonized, longing for the sound of a familiar voice.

Then magically, her prayer was answered, in the form of Wearmouth, a sympathetic friend from the Class of '56, popping in to save the day. Wearmouth, a much admired country neighbor, was mindful of her own forlorn first day as she offered gentle words of encouragement. But it was her loveliness in her crisp white uniform and white duty shoes that inspired Jensen the most. *Yes*, she vowed, *I'll stick this out for a year*. But when she crawled into bed that night — her very own bed, in her very own room, with her very own sink — she drifted off with a change of heart, *No*, she decided, *I'll stay for two*.

One classmate long remembered her very own sink with even greater gratitude that first day. Terror stricken over disobeying the rigid 10:00 p.m. curfew dictate, and battling an uncontrollable case of nerves that sent her bladder into overdrive at 11:00 p. m., she deemed her sink the only solution to her impossible dilemma.

Wright came from a unique set of circumstances that contributed to an especially troublesome beginning for her. She was an only child, with a mother who suffered severe hearing loss and a father whose medical practice kept him out of the home for long hours, so her entire life experience had been one of quiet solitude. Overnight she was tossed into the bedlam of a ten-story house packed with a frenzy of noisy nursing students. Conversing with anyone, or concentrating on anything, was a major challenge for Wright above the confusion of a corridor constantly humming with the unfamiliar sounds of her new mates. She was forever grateful for Thompson, the girl across the hall, whose patience and understanding pulled her through those early nerve-wracking days. Thompson died of breast cancer in April, 1988, the first classmate to say good-bye. Wright lost an unforgettable friend. We all did.

My personal remembrance of that first day was of hesitantly stepping through the south doors of the residence and taking the extended hand of Miss R. Catherine Aikin, Associate Director of Nursing Education. (We later dubbed her "Kate.") She stood stiffly in starched white from head to toe, her perfect French cuffs looking suspiciously like they'd never seen bedside duty. "Welcome, Miss King," she said, her cool glare sending chills down my spine. "It's nice to see you again. We're pleased you have chosen the Calgary General for your nursing education."

Yikes! I saw this woman only once for a ten minute interview — months ago — and she knows my name! I wasn't smug enough to think that I was especially memorable. I surmised that she'd memorized all 115 names and faces, no doubt aided from photos submitted with our application forms. I soon learned that an exercise such as this was a ho hum, everyday occurrence for Kate Aikin. She locked in *everything* on the first pass. I fought a compulsion to salute whenever I encountered her.

Registration took place from 2:00-3:00 p.m., when we received our room assignments, seemingly established alphabetically, although there were a number of exceptions. Our floor had one representative each for "B", "K" and "N", three "Ls" and a whole mess of "Ms". Then I think Kate must have reached the end of the alphabet and discovered a stray she had to squeeze in somewhere, which explains how Zelenka landed across the hall from King. In any event, I have been forever grateful, since I'm certain no one could have taken command of an elevator as capably as "Zeke." Ultimately, the rooms we were assigned that first day determined our closest relationships. The girls of North Four became my family.

At 3:00 p.m. we smoothed down our best — if not *only* — dresses, straightened the seams of our stockings, and tottered off to the sunken lounge in high heels for a formal reception tea.

This was by far the most terrifying part of the day. The summoned press captured two of my classmates receiving tea with a grey-haired, stately woman looking on, the notation under their picture reading, "Nervous, young, would-be nurses are put at their ease by Miss Gertrude Hall, Director of Nursing." I look at that caption today, and I think, *Huh? At ease? Who was that writer talking to?* Then I'm taken back to the symphony of clattering teacups gripped in shaking hands, a grim reminder of evidence to the contrary. Gertrude Hall, rest her soul, most assuredly did not put those nervous, young would-be nurses at ease on that day... nor on any of the subsequent 1,095 days. Nor did I ever perceive that to be her intent. We were in the army now, and we snapped to attention.

Sunken Lounge

Gertrude Hall's philosophy was, "Better education for nurses, better care for patients," but beyond that, she had a threefold plan to instil in her students: the toughness of the military, the softness of the compassionate, and the gentility of the finishing school graduate. I'm quite certain the latter was her toughest challenge, evidenced early, when a particular threesome straggled in on opening day.

....unfamiliar tea ritual.

Tomlinson remembers arriving a little late, with Shepard and Ward, hauling a bounty of clothing with a serious shortage of luggage. Loose apparel had been heaped in the trunk and back seat of their car, and the mountainous tangle of togs was now rolling through the residence foyer on a trolley. As they made their way to the elevators, they caught sight of their future classmates daintily sipping tea in the sunken lounge. Distracted by the tea party, they failed to notice the collection of items skidding off the trolley, leaving a trail in its wake. As Tomlinson describes the scene today, I visualize a stupefied Miss Hall rolling her eyes at Miss Aikin, as they witness, in disbelief, the "three stooges" clumsily scooping their snake of articles from the floor. In silent agreement, they nod, *Those three are going to need a lot of work.*

As our endurance with this unfamiliar tea ritual was approaching its limit, our "big sisters," fresh from hospital duties, bounded in with some much needed comic relief. The nursing school had long embraced the custom of a second year student adopting an incoming junior student as her "little sister," someone she would take under her wing and be prepared to mentor for the first two years. We had all received letters from our big sisters prior to registration, and now they appeared in person to guide us through these first days of learning the ropes.

Many big and little sisters formed a strong bond during student days, and the custom in general produced a sisterhood mentality that we would embrace forever after. For me, having grown up with only brothers, a houseful of sisters was a windfall. Even Zelenka, my new-found buddy across the hall, freely adopted me as a sister, even though she already had five back home on the farm. And so it was, that overnight, this bevy of "nervous, young, would-be nurses" — with little else in common — became sisters for life.

Activities night in the play room, organized by our big sisters, was our introduction to the entire student body and to the school's extracurricular activities. The zany antics of our senior sisters that first night acted not only as a welcome antidote to the stiffness of Gertrude's afternoon tea, but also as a signal that "cutting loose" was the prescription of choice for maintaining balance in this new life. In the days to come, we dosed — and *over*dosed — often.

As if there weren't enough on everyone's plates as we learned about residence life, some of the out-of-town girls reckoned it imperative to take on their *entire* new world directly. Hustad and a group of her new friends set out on foot on their first day off to acquaint themselves with the big city. They began with a meander through the nearby zoo, which eventually funnelled them onto Ninth Avenue and into the downtown core. After checking out every last shop of interest, they worked their way back to the residence, arriving at dusk, footsore, but bubbling to tell the awaiting matron all about their day's adventure. They were taken aback with her response. The poor quaking soul was aghast at the thought of her innocent little charges casually wandering the east end streets of town at this hour of the day. Looking back now, I think we were quite oblivious to the nursing school's sense of responsibility for our safety. We thought we were grownups now; we could look after ourselves.

In any event, the Hustad explorers continued with their quest to experience big city life. They would investigate the local churches next, and ease in with two familiar denominations they'd known in their respective home towns: the Anglican and the United Churches. They felt quite at home the first two Sundays, and their presumed safety brought comfort to the fretful matron. However, since their initial intent was to broaden their city experience, on the third Sunday they ventured into uncharted territory, that of a curious church they'd spotted in the neighborhood. "Well, here goes," said Hustad, as she swung open the door to an intriguing new adventure. The service was already underway, but they were greeted cordially and ushered to a pew.

"What's this all about?" one of the girls whispered, sizing up the lay of the land as she peered quizzically over her hymn book. "I'd rather sit over there," she pointed with a muffled giggle. Heads craned to see what was "over there," and only then did they twig to their circumstance. They were entirely surrounded by women and children, safely out of temptation of all male members of the congregation who were ensconced across the aisle "over there." When they further observed that all the women were completely devoid of make-up or jewellery, they snickered nervously as they attempted to hide their conspicuous cherry lips and glittering

Sunday-best earrings. The day marked the beginning and the end of their house-of-worship adventures on unfamiliar turf.

Getting Down to Business

The first week was a blur of activity in preparation for the official launch the following week. In four prearranged groups, we paraded through the school and the residence for orientation, attended preparatory conferences with directors and instructors, and pored over compulsory reading tests. I remember being so exhausted writing one electronically-marked reading test, that by the last few pages I took to coloring in the little squares at random in order to complete the thing before I slid into a coma. I was terrified when Miss Aikin later summoned me to her office for my results.

"Miss King," she began, sombrely — once again with that cool glare — "fifty percent of the population reads at a level as high as or higher than you. If you are to maintain the academic level indicated on your high school transcript, I suggest you add some practice reading to your daily schedule." I improved greatly on a subsequent test. I had not done a lick of practice reading, but I did read every question with due care before coloring in the squares. Miss Aikin was impressed.

There was also a list of minutiae pressing for our immediate attention:

1. Registration fees — steep at $15.00, but subsidized if necessary.
2. Name tags that omitted first names — MISS E. R. KING — which, combined with the professional staff custom of addressing us as "Miss King," prompted us to address one another off duty by surnames only — "Hey, King!"

3. Fittings for uniforms, which required laundry labels that, lo and behold, revealed our first names, albeit hidden in the collar. The labels also bore a number that identified not only our laundry, but everything else from exam papers to test results. I was "Eleanor King 469" which sounded a bit like an inmate's ID — fitting perhaps, since the regimented, restricted life in residence definitely took on an air of incarceration.

4. The purchase of white duty shoes, selection to be made from a wide array of one choice, an oxford made by Clinic, ringing in at $12.95. (I have since learned what a shocking increase this was over the 1934 price of $5.50.)

The end of the beginning was now in sight.

The final item on the week's agenda was the unpleasant business of medicals. Most of us were healthy, young women who had rarely, if ever, seen doctors since our childhood encounters with the family pediatrician. Suddenly we were confronted with immunization shots, chest x-rays and the indignity of scrutiny by a line-up of alien doctors. Tigner relates the humiliation of parading from cubicle to cubicle in a skimpy gown to be poked and prodded by one male specialist after another. "I was coping," she said, "until the doctor examining my back had me bend over and my gown fell open. I could not believe I was standing in front of this strange man with all of me hanging out!" Since modesty ruled the day for girls of the fifties, this mortifying encounter came within a heartbeat of nipping Tigner's career in the bud.

Some weeks later, Peterson's modesty was also assailed when her floor mates stole her towel and all her clothes while she was taking a shower. Peterson surveyed the bathroom for a solution to her dilemma. Aha! Pinned to the wall of each of the three toilet cubicles were strips of newspaper for wrapping sanitary napkins. Newspapers pinned together would make a very fine garment for preserving one's decency. The paparazzi awaiting outside the bathroom door with cameras in hand did not get the Playboy shot they were anticipating. They had to content themselves with snapping their subject fleeing down the hall clad in the news of the day.

The planning of the new residence and its attached school was a joint venture between administration and architects, with input from the students. The passageway between the school and the residence held administration offices, our wall of private mailboxes, an in/out board, and a reception/switchboard desk presided over by our beloved Mrs. Sanders. From her post, Mrs. Sanders could keep an eye on the spacious reception foyer, the connector to everything else, from the regulation-sized auditorium on the west to the dorm elevators on the north.

The foyer spilled into a spectacular sunken lounge with parquet flooring and furniture strategically arranged in groupings to encourage families to meet and greet. Overlooking the lounge to the north perched a row of small reception rooms, sometimes referred to as "provincial" rooms for their clever decor representing

the provinces of Canada. However, their most common designation
was "beau" rooms, and they were the talk of the town.

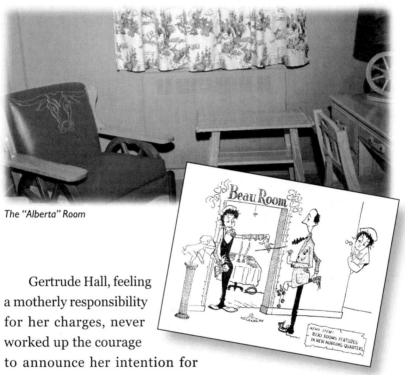

The "Alberta" Room

Gertrude Hall, feeling
a motherly responsibility
for her charges, never
worked up the courage
to announce her intention for
these innovative — if not daring — rooms in plain language,
but it didn't take a rocket scientist to get the message. She wanted
her little darlings to say goodnight to their dates in the privacy of
Quebec, rather than in the back seat of a Meteor. Curiously, the
beau rooms seemed empty much of the time, even on a Saturday
night when one might have expected a line to form from British
Columbia to Newfoundland. In retrospect, it's clear to me now why
Gertrude located the residence chapel adjacent to the beau rooms.
Additionally, Fraser just now told me that Gertrude sent a select
group of girls to Northminster United Church to attend its Youth

Sex Education program, offered by Dr. Bob Hatfield. I don't know what her selection criteria were, but I did not meet them. Mine is not to reason why.

The little chapel, parked on its lonesome in the far corner, was a gem. Furnished lovingly by our Alumnae Association, it featured a glorious stained glass window designed by a notable association member, Eleanor Tregillis (Robertson '37).

Chapel

Rounding out the main floor was an inviting reading room which I was always drawn to, but curling up with a good book was a luxury our schedule rarely allowed. This, and all the common rooms in the residence, contained furnishings generously donated by citizens of Calgary, including a grand piano, a collection of Gissing paintings, and a dazzling, ornate mirror reflecting all the grandeur of the setting.

The basement housed all our practical areas, beginning with our little Tuck Shop, which we staffed ourselves on a rotating basis. It carried all our essentials, such as shampoo, shoe polish, and Crispy Crunch chocolate bars. Then there was the laundry room for our personal laundry, and a shampoo room for our hair. That's right, we were to shampoo our bodies upstairs and our heads downstairs — the result of Gertrude Hall's grand design to protect ten floors worth of plumbing from wadding up with the snarling mass of three hundred heads worth of squeaky clean hair. The rest of the basement — a three-piece study in contrasts — contained our shared socializing space.

Reading Room

The pajama lounge was hugely popular, with its adjoining kitchen that supplied us with snack food and beverages (not that kind). The lounge was furnished with the only television set in the building, and it was the one common room where we could hang out in any state of dress or undress. There was a games room with ping pong and shuffleboard that was also a favorite, and finally, in a secluded corner stood Gertrude Hall's pride and joy, a formal dining room elegantly outfitted with fine china, crystal and silverware. Gertrude had a vision of producing not only fine nurses, but fine young women. Her dream for the dining room was to turn out gracious hostesses who could entertain in the grandest fashion. Thank goodness graduation from the school did not hinge on her pipe dream. My only memory of ever entering the dining room after that first day's tour, was to chase down a stray ping pong ball. To Gertrude's delight, however, some of her girls rose to the occasion in her cherished room.

Pajama Lounge

Hustad remembers her mother and sister-in-law turning out a turkey dinner there with all the trimmings to celebrate her twenty-first birthday. The two cooks were bowled over by such a fully equipped kitchen, not to mention the lavish serving dishes, linens and tableware. This really was Buckingham Palace. The eight lucky classmates making up the guest list must have been equally impressed. Imagine how good that turkey dinner would have tasted after a diet of cafeteria food served on Melmac trays.

McElheran became engaged on Valentine's Day of our final year, and decided only a formal dinner in Gertrude's dining room would do justice to the occasion. The guest list was drawn up, and the easiest task was selecting the two guests of honor; it would be the couple who had introduced her to her fiancé. The room was booked well in advance, and a proud Gertrude Hall made an appearance to assure that every knife and fork was in its rightful place.

McElheran hasn't forgotten how terrified she was, counting each piece of china as she removed it from the locked cabinet. Her hands had never before felt the magic of *Minton*, and they did not rest until each piece had been carefully hand washed, counted, and returned to the cabinet at evening's end. The meal itself played second fiddle to the setting, although the heavenly roast chicken and mashed potatoes (eclipsing the overcooked peas) were an undeniable success, and the proud husband-to-be knew he'd made a choice as fine as the china.

The Groom & Bride

C. Smith returned to the residence after graduation to celebrate the biggest day of her life. She and her husband were married in the little chapel on the main floor, then led their guests down the flowing staircase to the inviting dining room for a reception. It was a small, intimate affair, with sandwiches, sweets and tea prepared by the mother-of-the-bride's church group. Their simple, unpretentious church offering was transformed into a spread fit for a queen on the Minton china. It was a day to remember.

Crowning our Buckingham Palace, was a glorious rooftop sun deck with a spectacular view of the riverbank, the cityscape, and on the horizon, the mountains that kept the rest of the world at bay. The deck was a favorite place to veg out on a summer's day off or grab a relaxing breath before tackling evening duty. And it was the place to go if you were into power tanning, because it got you closer to the sun.

Our glorious sun deck...

House Rules

Growing up, I remember my mother occasionally speaking of two acquaintances who had names I thought were so hilarious I used to accuse her of making them up. One was Goldie Silvers and the other was Birdie Finch. I nearly fell over the day we were introduced to our three residence supervisors — the private-eyes who would track our every move for three years — Mrs. Clapham, Mrs. Dickson and Mrs. Finch. *Birdie Finch* — the one and only. Imagine, face to face with *the* Birdie Finch! *Forgive me, Mother, you didn't make it up.* And you might know Mrs. Finch's first words to me: "Are you related to Ruby King?" Wash my mouth with soap, should I tell a lie. "Yes, she's my mother," I confessed reluctantly, dying to add, *I know, she's an angel, but don't expect the same of her offspring.* I had already dashed the expectations of high school teachers who knew my angel mother. *Here we go again.*

Photo: courtesy Melinda Price

I don't remember seeing Mrs. Finch attired in anything but an impossibly stiff, long-sleeved uniform with a cap similar to Miss Hall's, which led us to believe they trained at the same school. Bold red lipstick and rouge highlighted her pale skin and white hair, and she had a deep, resonating voice that struck fear in every heart. Nothing escaped her eye as she combed the halls issuing reprimands for rule infractions, or leaving notes on our desks following room inspection: "Books belong on your bookshelf, not on your bed"; "Your bedspread is dragging on the floor"; "Please clean the toothpaste splatter from the wall above your sink"; "There's a screw loose in the arm of your chair." *A what? Where?* The latter missive left for Fraser, had her mumbling, *What about all the other loose screws around this place?*

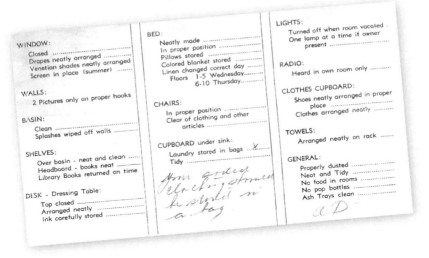

Of course, all this fastidious checking probably saved a life the night she caught a group of us dangling D. Miller head first down the laundry chute from the eighth floor, our grip on her ankles slipping away as we grew weak with laughter. After hauling Miller back up to safety, a ghostly white, trembling Mrs. Finch retreated down the

Checklist: courtesy Edith Schroeder

hall, shaking her head in disbelief. I can imagine the phone call to Gertrude Hall that must have played through her mind. *That's right, they dropped her from the eighth floor! Yes, down the laundry chute. Is she what? Well, eight floors... she must be dead.*

Yet, Mrs. Finch had a ready sense of humor, and I can still hear her breaking into a guttural giggle when confronted with some of our antics. Ward reminded me of the time she pulled an antic of her own, by crashing a Halloween party. She was wrapped in a fur coat with a stocking pulled over her head. *Mrs. Finch out of uniform? Her flawless coiffure disturbed?* I would not have believed such a sight had Ward not captured it on camera.

Mrs. Finch had a ready ready sense of humor...

I think back on Mrs. Dickson as a quiet, grandmotherly type who assuredly spotted our misdemeanors, but didn't have the heart to press charges. She no doubt operated on the correct assumption that Mrs. Finch was keeping everything under tabs.

Zelenka remembers the night she and McCullagh were dutifully in their respective rooms at curfew, albeit dangling out their doors in animated conversation. Mrs. Dickson, who resided in the apartment adjacent to McCullagh's room, couldn't help but overhear the muffled talk, but true to form, instead of rightfully charging them with a minor offence, she invited them into her sitting room for tea and cookies. Zelenka has only just revealed this incriminating evidence all these years later, fearing "teacher's pet" accusations from her classmates. Of course, it's never too late.

McElheran confirmed that our residence supervisors were more than inspector generals, they were doting mother substitutes in times of need. She has not forgotten the night that, suffering severe abdominal pain, she summoned Mrs. Dickson, who scurried her through the tunnel by wheelchair to Emergency. Dr. W. O. Rothwell wasted no time in removing a festering appendix.

Mrs. Clapham was our night supervisor, so I have little memory of encountering her, except at the entrance to our chapel every morning at 7:15 a.m. When working day shift, we were required to attend chapel — a bible reading, hymn and prayer — in full uniform, having closed our doors on rooms in perfect order. A strict dress code began with the ever-loving girdle, garters and stockings under a full, tailored slip. (My Aunt Lil bemoaned the advent of pantyhose which spelled the end of the girdle, claiming, "A girdle tells you when you have had enough to eat.")

Next came the blue check gingham dress, which called for the tedious insertion of buttons — removable for laundering — entirely down the front and on the cuffs. Most of us will confess, however, to taking the shortcut of inserting only alternate buttons, since they were concealed by a top layer —

the bib and apron, stiff as cardboard and twice as thick. A pleat had to be folded into the bib, then a safety pin pushed through the resulting three layers and on through the waistband of the apron to which it was attached, and to which four more buttons had been laboriously inserted at the back. Many a pin was bent during this exercise, and many a finger tingled its objection. Some girls used to lubricate pins in their bar of hand soap, but I never thought it helped enough to warrant shredding the soap.

Finally, the cap — our cap had to be folded and pinned around a specially sized square of cardboard, then anchored to the hair with three bobby pins. Name tags, class pins, and bandage scissors tucked into the back of the waistband completed the outfit, with the exception of one unofficial addition carried by most of us — a chain of safety pins dangling from the pocket of our dresses, hidden beneath our aprons. Pins were invaluable for all manner of emergencies on duty, most notably the plight of the gaping gown/bare bottom. Since I detested mornings, my attire was not only pre-buttoned and pre-pinned the night before, but meticulously laid out in donning order. There was a limit to how long Zelenka could hold the elevator.

Mrs. Clapham, a picture of perfection, stood erect at the chapel door, eyes peeled to a bowl she held in outstretched hands, a bowl into which we dropped our names, printed on a scrap of paper. The assumption was that she picked through every name in the bowl after chapel, to confirm whether everyone obliged to attend had done so.

One morning I arrived with two scraps of paper — the second one carrying the name of a delinquent classmate who had coerced me into covering for her — and I had to plunge my hand deep into the bowl, and give it a swish to conceal my two-name drop. Mrs. Clapham's eyes shot up, meeting mine squarely with an I'm-on-to-you glare. She was helpless to interrupt the process, however, with a continuous flow of names dropping into her bowl from classmates filing by, but that glare prevented me from repeating the action ever again. I had attended high school with Mrs. Clapham's son Bill, and on mornings like that, I wondered what stories she told him over the breakfast table.

Our compact rooms were ingeniously designed to fulfil our every need: a sink/desk unit with a flip-up top that became a mirrored vanity; a wardrobe with built-in drawers; and a bed that doubled as a couch with pillow storage cupboards as its backrest. The item of utmost importance, however, was the buzzer located above the desk — our precious link to the outside world.

...the buzzer located above the desk — our precious link to the outside world.

This clever little device, controlled by our switchboard operator, buzzed once to signal a phone call, and twice to announce a visitor in the lobby. It had a dime-sized black disk (some of us mysteriously remember as red) in the centre that dropped when your room was buzzed, showing white, and returned when you pressed your buzzer in response. It was the first thing we looked for on entering our rooms after an absence, a white disk sending us on a dash for the phone. "Mrs. Sanders, who was calling me?" There was a complication with the buzzer, however, which for me was significant. You see, it was installed in the common wall between your own room and that of your classmate next door, so that it was difficult to distinguish just whose buzzer was buzzing. The color of the disk was the only foolproof indicator.

As luck would have it, I shared a wall with Lovewell, a blonde bombshell who turned heads when she walked by. *Lady Clairol* would have given her eye teeth to bottle the color of that hair. Do you know how many times the brunette next door bolted for her buzzer, only to slump in dejection at the red disk (or was it black?) staring back at her... followed by Lovewell's streaking past her door on her way to the phone?

Early in the first week, we returned from class one day to discover a pink-covered booklet positioned squarely on our desks. It was the Student Handbook (henceforth referred to as our Pink Book) — a fifty-page directive detailing everything from student bylaws, residence hours, and use of the telephone, to major and minor offences, and instructions on how to study. I always thought the school's expectation of responsible maturity under a pink book of rules fit for a junior high boarding school to be a dichotomy between theory and practice. And I'm as flabbergasted today as I was then with the quote on the first page:

> Ignorance of the law excuses no man;
> not that all men know the law, but
> because 'tis an excuse every man will
> plead, and no man can tell how to refute him.
> — John Selden

The book goes on to couch rules, regulations, dictates and commands with softer terminology such as "customs, responsibilities, policies and privileges," closing with a subtle suggestion, "... whenever you are in doubt as to the acceptable course

The "Pink Book"

of action, you ask for guidance first, thus saving yourself and others from embarrassment or discomfort" — a statement that defies comment. But as I flip through the book today, it is the words on page 29 that leap off the page: "Do not hold the elevators. They are fast and will return quickly." Whew! Thank heaven Zelenka never bothered to read her Pink Book... at least not all the way to page 29.

Page 16 covers use of the telephones — the five-digit residence number was 67541 — beseeching us to inform the switchboard operator of our whereabouts, and reminding us that "there are 300 students and one switchboard operator. There is a limit to personal service... " But Mrs. Sanders, our much loved operator, apparently did not read the Pink Book either, because she gave us personal service for three years.

Mrs. Sanders not only had an uncanny knack for knowing who we were and where we were at all times, but she quickly learned the faces of every young man who came calling. When spotting a steady beau coming up the walk, she sometimes "buzzed" for his date before he even entered the residence. One night, however, her system backfired.

Mrs. Sanders had been enthusiastically following my continuing courtship with a steady friend from high school days. Unfortunately, she wasn't privy to a recent change in our state of affairs:

"Do you think we've been dating exclusively for too long?" I suggest, gingerly.

"I dunno. Is that what you're feeling?"

"Well, I kinda think so. Why don't we circulate for a bit, and see what happens?"

"I guess, if that's what you want, but the trouble is, we've gone together for so long, I don't know any other girls now."

"Well, I can help you with that," I offer with a shrug, "I live in a house full of girls!" And so I provide my friend with a few names that I think would make compatible dates.

Eight o'clock the following Saturday evening rolls around, and my buzzer bleeps twice, signalling a caller. *Hm-m,* I wonder, as I press it in response, *who's this? I'm not expecting anyone.* I throw on a skirt and head for the elevator in excited anticipation of some secret admirer waiting in the lobby. Kell steps onto the elevator on the next floor.

"Well, look at you all gussied up," I exclaim. "Big date? Who's the lucky guy?"

"Damned if I know," Kell chortles, with that impish grin of hers, "some guy who got my name from someone."

We prattle on, as we walk together down the hall leading to the lobby. "Have fun," I smirk with a roll of the eyes as I shoulder the swinging lobby door, "Don't stay out past curfew."

Then suddenly the hair rises on the back of my neck as I tumble to the scenario I am a heartbeat from encountering — a circumstance of my own invention. *Dummy,* I mutter to myself, as I turn tail and retreat swiftly and silently from sight.

I had palpitations the rest of the night at the thought of approaching my old beau side by side with his date of the evening. But I can't begin to imagine what poor Mrs. Sanders was experiencing after cleverly buzzing my room, then in horror, discovering her mistake, and buzzing the requested room, followed by responses from both! She must have been sweating bullets as she awaited the *ménage à trois* in the lobby.

Thiessen remembers Mrs. Sanders with great fondness, suggesting perhaps she found a kindred spirit through their shared German origins. One night, coming off evening shift, Mrs. Sanders informed Thiessen that the "Black Widow Opera" was on TV, whispering in collaboration, "You go on down and watch it. No one else needs to know." It's not surprising that Thiessen remembers this event still today — watching illicit television after midnight under the security of a trustworthy sympathizer is the kind of rare occurrence we would all carry in our thoughts to our dying day.

The Pink Book also contained an extensive list of commands regarding attire, beginning with "uniforms shall be worn." The list went on: no jewellery, nail polish or excessive make-up; hair worn above the collar or otherwise secured by a hair net; plain white cardigans on night duty only, but not while giving direct nursing care. Attire for the main areas of the residence or the cafeteria was just as uncompromising: no slacks, shorts, jeans, slippers, house coats or pin curls, and a demand in bold print, "stockings, **not socks** should be worn." The very least of our attire to be worn *anywhere* was housecoats and slippers. Slippers... blessed slippers!

Our supervisors were fixated on slippers: "NEVER, NEVER, NEVER walk around in bare feet." — Pink Book, page 19. I experienced firsthand how serious they were the evening I impulsively tore barefoot down the hall to the phone stand to receive an eagerly awaited call.

I am nicely settled into conversation with the drop-dead gorgeous jock I met recently at a school dance, when Mrs. Finch's unmistakable voice resonates from behind, "Miss King, tell your caller to hold the line while you go back to your room and get your slippers." Before I can react, a falsetto voice on the other end sings, "Miss King, run along now and get your slippies." Funny, I now have no memory whether my conversation with Mr. Falsetto ever led to a date, or even who he was. But if the image of an evening at the Capitol Theatre with a girl wearing bedroom slippers led him to bolt, I have forgiven him.

One classmate was so programmed with the slipper rule that when she was suddenly confronted with a patient wandering the halls late one evening without a stitch on, she shrieked with alarm, "Mr. Starkers, you haven't got your slippers on!"

The most elaborate set of rules revolved around "social privileges," namely "late leaves" and "sleep-outs," the latter being permitted only prior to days off or shift rotation. Four 12:00 a.m. late leaves per month were granted for juniors, with the curfew creeping to 1:00 a.m. for seniors until the final six months, when "discretion" was allowed. Otherwise, all students were to be in their rooms behind closed doors by 11:00 p.m. A complicated list of major and minor offences centred around abuse of privileges, while penalties consisted of withdrawal of those privileges.

Minor offences were truly minor: visiting after hours, loud radios, failure to mark the "in/out" board, or untidy rooms. And our rooms had to pass a *Westpoint Barracks* inspection to meet the criteria for tidy. Something as minor as an unemptied ashtray was an offence, and elicited a note of condemnation, especially from Mrs. Finch, the slipper sleuth. "Miss Erb, please empty your ashtray. BF"

Drawers were searched for banned substances — food — which caused a major stir if found. Our supervisors, from past experience in the old residences, were paranoid about stale food breeding nasty little critters in our drawers that would quickly multiply and spread to the closet, the bed and the sink before crawling under the door, down the hall and onto the elevators, eventually overtaking the entire residence. Find a cupcake in your bottom drawer, and their imaginations ran amok with horror movie images: "Attack of the Cosmic Cockroaches"; "Invasion of the Starving Silverfish."

Once a week we were delivered fresh linens: one sheet, one pillowcase, one facecloth and two towels. Fitted sheets did not exist, so the rule of thumb was to rotate sheets just the way my practical mother taught me: bottom sheet to the laundry; top sheet to the bottom; clean sheet on top. A missive from Birdie Finch was delivered with the bed linens whenever the situation warranted. "Miss Matthews, why isn't your bed stripped? BF" The Pink Book cautioned against hoarding linen, because "it will be found during the checking of rooms and reported to the Arbitration Board." Finally, if you ever gave thought to cleaning up your room *after* morning chapel, rather than *before*, as required, you likely did that only once. You would have made the enlightening discovery that the intervening ten minutes was all the time it took for Mrs. Finch to scour the entire ten floors, discover your misdemeanor, leave you one of her infamous notes, and issue a penalty. How did she do that? It's humanly impossible.

Major offences concerned hour restrictions, and were spelled out with ironclad precision: 5 minutes late drew the loss of one late leave; between 5 and 15 minutes, the loss of two; and between 15 and 30 minutes resulted in life without parole — three lost late leaves. Thirty-one minutes late sent you directly to the Arbitration Board where you were expected to get the death penalty... except the Board was made up of representatives from each class, who listened sympathetically to phony alibis, and usually voted for acquittal. In the event you were convicted, Article IV, Section I allowed, "In case of dissatisfaction of a decision of the Board, it is the student's privilege to request a repeal of the decision and appeal to the Students' Council." It didn't take Johnny Cochrane to spring you. All in all, the Board was a pretty ineffectual body, but it nevertheless gave us a proud sense of self-government.

Seniors were allowed more latitude with late leaves, but were consequently penalized more heavily for their abuse. Half an hour cost you *seven* late leaves, comically spelled out this way: one for the first 5 minutes, one for the second five, one for the third five, and *four* for the next fifteen. Oh, to have been a bug on the wall as the masterminds cooked up this unfathomable formula.

Collver developed a foolproof method for avoiding late penalties. She and her high school sweetheart concluded every date parked in his car at the end of the sidewalk leading to the north doors of the residence. At precisely 30 seconds to the witching hour — you could set your watch by it — the passenger door of a blue TR2 convertible would fly open, releasing Collver to sprint for the residence, where she'd fly past the supervisor, breathless and dishevelled, but under the wire. Apparently, *breathless and dishevelled* did not constitute an offence, major or minor, so there was no motivation to alter the routine. This remained her method of operation for the entire three years.

Finally, I vaguely remember roaming the residence halls after hours on "proctor duty," a rotating assignment we always carried out with a member from another class. The purpose was to inspect the residence at the end of the day, carrying out tasks such as turning off dripping taps in the bathrooms, unplugging irons about to set fire to the place, or reporting anyone out of their room after hours. We were on the honor system regarding the latter, with the non-classmate of an offender designated to register the offence. I'm happy to report that we were indeed honorable — no one ever ratted on a sister from any class even if we spotted her turning summersaults down the hall at midnight. I remember looking over my shoulder as I made rounds, fully expecting to find Mrs. Finch following in my footsteps — proctoring the proctor — but she never showed. Maybe it was past her bedtime. The upside to proctor duty for me was getting to stay up past my bedtime.

There was one further rule, one that was firmly implanted long before the Pink Book: the rule prohibiting marriage. Student nurses of the day were principally an exclusive, all-female singles club. However, the Class of '59 was blessed with an exception to the rule in Banister, a beloved sister who entered the school as a married woman with three teenage daughters. Many years prior, Banister had entered nursing school at age eighteen, but had left prematurely to marry. It was a decision that nagged her off and on through the years, eventually weighing so heavily upon her, she set out to finish her dream. After careful consideration, our school accepted her on the condition she begin at the beginning, which she agreed to willingly. We embraced Banister as a sister, although she was almost old enough to be our mother. I'm sure there were countless times when it was abundantly evident to her that we needed mothering, but she never assumed that role. At least she was spared our silly antics in residence at the end of her day; she was allowed to go home and deal with the antics of her three waiting daughters.

Now there was a rule that allowed us to marry during our last six months, but it wasn't waved under our noses in bold print, and few of us were aware of it until Peterson slipped out one day the end of May and tied the knot with her impatient prince. Only Peterson was scrupulous enough to read the fine print. It was there all along:

> Marriage is allowed during the final six months under the following conditions:
> 1. parents are in agreement
> 2. parents are willing to release the school from custodial responsibilities
> 3. no special privileges are granted
> 4. academic progress must be maintained
> 5. good health must be maintained
> 6. general conduct must be high

I have not lost sleep over this critical statute escaping my notice, since any notion of marriage I might have entertained would have been shot down in flames by the first condition. I was evidently not alone. Throughout the year following our graduation, church aisles near and far were flooded with my sisters streaming to the altar.

Unruly House

Once every fourth week, a small parcel in brown paper wrapping was placed on our beds on top of the fresh linen. It was our month's supply of sanitary napkins. Regrettably, the supervisors neglected to enclose instructions for the use of these odd little wads of cotton, so a surprising number of the uninformed set about stuffing them into their bras, polishing their shoes, or tying them tail to tail into elaborate party streamers. I'm embarrassed to reveal how many classmates encountered the infamous Kotex chain strung from ceiling light to reading lamp to closet door and back again, on returning to their rooms from evening duty or days off. However, I'm willing to forgive these momentary lapses in sanity, since extended incarceration has to be the rationale for such aberrant behavior from grown women.

Yes, we natives got restless within the confines of long hours and strict house rules, and with limited time and resources to ease the tension, room wreckage was all too often the therapy of choice. Some rooms experienced full-blown shock treatments. While this may have been a therapeutic release for the perpetrator, it delivered added stress to the weary victim. McElheran was not amused when the Kotex marauder decorated her room on her birthday, carting her bed to the basement to make room for celebrations. To this day she doesn't know who to accuse, and no one's owning up. And it's hard to believe that Thiessen, noted for her quiet, calm demeanor, totally lost it the night she returned to a room of devastation after a Class of '59 celebration. Since we classmates celebrating with her had an alibi, our little sisters became prime suspects. The nerve! Had they no respect?

Every floor seemed to have one classmate who qualified as its chief practical joker, the person who either spearheaded mass attacks or pulled secret capers single-handedly. Dingwall took the honors on her floor, and her hall mates soon adopted the philosophy that if you can't prove guilt, then blame Dingwall.

One evening, Doherty was working a 4-8 p.m. shift. The room across the hall from hers had been stripped bare for painting, and her neighbors, Falck, Finch, Hustad and Zoeteman were bored. You have guessed — a formula for trouble. The fiendish foursome carted every scrap of Doherty's belongings from her box spring and mattress to her comb and toothbrush across the hall, dumping the works into the vacant room. *Not a whisper was left behind. Then they retreated to their respective rooms and waited. At 8:15 p.m. Doherty waltzed off the elevator and down the hall to her room, good naturedly announcing her arrival by tapping on doors in passing, while calling out each tenant's name. Then the tapping stopped, and there was a long silence... pierced by an ear-splitting wail, "DING-G-G-WAL-L-L!" Did the perpetrators feel guilty when a totally innocent Dingwall was fingered for this crime? Not for a minute.

> *Pink Book, page 29 : "Furniture is not to be moved
> without permission from the Residence Supervisor."

But no one outdid McCullagh, the resident prankster on my floor, who struck silently, swiftly and repeatedly like a thief in the night, pulling off capers that defied imagination. Zelenka and I were her immediate neighbors, and therefore her most frequent victims. Zelenka still breathes fire when she relates her best (or worst) McCullagh story today.

Zelenka had worked a particularly brutal evening shift, and during the lonely walk back to residence through the tunnel, she plotted her deliverance from the day's trials: she would first soothe her aching feet with a comforting soak in the sink, then free her mind by nestling into bed with a gripping novel. She could hardly wait. She threw open her door and flipped the light switch. Nothing. Flipped it a couple more times. Pitch black. She groped her way across the room to the floor lamp. Click... nothing. She felt for the bulb. Gone. She reached for her last remaining hope — her bed lamp. Click... a 15-watt glow seeped across her pillow.

Zelenka stormed out of her room and pounded on McCullagh's door, cussing her name under her breath. There was no response; McCullagh was splitting her sides in silence under the covers. She would suffocate before revealing guilt by coming up for air. Zelenka tossed through a sleepless night, arising exhausted and in a terrible frame of mind. She would have to call upon her secret method for working off steam — her personal anger management therapy. She stomped off to the zoo and taunted the peacocks. If their feathers fell off, she decided, it would be McCullagh's fault.

I haven't forgotten the time I returned from a night on the town without a minute to spare to make my assigned night shift, which would begin at midnight. I embraced the philosophy that every precious minute allowed in the outside world was not to be squandered, and this night I had really cut it fine. It was going to be touch and go whether I could throw on my uniform, sprint through the tunnel, and report for duty on time. The closets in our rooms had two large hinged doors that opened from the middle, and I grabbed both handles of mine, and flung wide. Wham! The doors were airborne, and I was back-pedalling to stay on my feet. In seconds, the doors had me pinned against my desk, gasping in shock. What the %#@*>#? Someone had removed the hinge pins. It was after hours, which meant I, like Zelenka before me, had to cuss McCullagh under my breath. But I did spare the peacocks.

McCullagh died in September, 1995, carrying to her grave the mysteries of who she bribed for a pass key or where on earth she scrounged a 15-watt light bulb. She never confessed to anything, but we knew her handiwork. The curious appearance of peace offerings such as a candy taped to a desktop with a note reading, "The Phantom Strikes Again!" never quite cut it. Sorry, McCullagh, we miss you greatly and love you dearly, but we haven't found it in our hearts to forgive. We're still ticked.

McCullagh's door was *always* locked. She didn't take a shower, make a phone call, or step across the hall to borrow a safety pin without locking her door. And since we didn't have her savvy for breaking and entering, any notions of getting even were perpetually thwarted. One night, however, when she was safely sealed inside her room, she finally got her just desserts. Four of us lined up outside her door armed with our waste paper baskets filled with water, and a fifth combatant knelt at the foot of her door with a pair of dustpans borrowed from housekeeping. Then the first avenger began pouring into the dustpans, strategically sloped in a "V" to direct the water flow under the door.

The goings on on the other side of the door must have been a sight to behold. McCullagh's only defence was two towels and a nearby sink, and we could hear a lot of huffing and puffing (though never a cry of surrender), as she methodically plopped one towel into the pooling water while wringing the other out in the sink. As fast as our four-man bucket brigade could circulate through the washroom for refills, she was single-handedly keeping the Red River at bay: sop, wring, sop, wring, sop, wring... My recollection is a skirmish that lasted for the better part of an hour, and I'm ashamed to admit that it was the wringing warrior who emerged victorious. The great flood ended with five exhausted hosers throwing in the towel.

Anyone who's ever lived in a dorm, has either pulled the Saran Wrap stretched over the toilet bowl (under the seat) stunt, or been the hapless victim of that prank. But for sheer tenacity, Zoeteman wins the prize. In fact, if the Guiness Book of Records had a "swathe the toilet" category, her name would be there. She and a sidekick — whose name she has conveniently forgotten — took on the entire residence in a wild 54-toilet "wrap and flee" spree. The cost of the wrap stole a hefty portion of their month's allowance, but it was worth every penny. The only bathrooms in the place that did not fall victim to the saboteurs were those in the private suites of the supervisors and Gertrude Hall, but knowing Zoeteman, she didn't pass their doors without giving pause. In the end, Gertrude Hall got wind of the pair's indefensible act, and put the lid on their fun. Fits of laughter abruptly turned to sober attention, as they stood quaking before their stern director. "Miss Zoeteman, do you have any idea what it would cost to unplug the toilets and drains of a ten-story building, if that Saran Wrap were to be flushed?" *Good heavens*, thought Zoeteman as she stood in stunned silence, *what is this woman thinking? Who would do such a stupid thing?* I can't help imagining poor Gertrude Hall prudently designing a shampoo room to keep the pesky plumbing clear of hair, only to have every toilet in the place gagging on Saran Wrap.

Some classmates became so traumatized by the steady succession of pranks, they began showing signs of losing their grip. Peterson relates the time she stole away with Scotland's photo of her boyfriend and her beloved plush toy "Flower" the skunk, after a visit to her room. When Scotland eventually became aware that these items were missing, it was her best friend Peterson she came to with her sob story. Peterson calmly and patiently listened to her entire tale of woe while cuddling "Flower" on her lap, the boyfriend smiling over her shoulder from his framed image on the desk. The scene staring Scotland smack in the face simply did not register... at least not until the middle of the night. At the crack of dawn she crept red-faced down to Peterson's door to collect her stolen treasures. Regrettably, Scotland did not stay the course to graduate with us; I only hope we are not to blame.

There was a definite pecking order in the hospital world, with the doctors at the top of the order and the lowly junior student nurses near the bottom. The order carried into the nurses' residence where Gertrude Hall occupied the penthouse suite and we junior students were relegated to the lower floors. Each floor had at least one distinguishing feature. For example, I believe it was South Five that had its own private safety deposit box. It held an extraordinary collection of eyelash curlers, mascara, lipstick, earrings, sweaters, jeans, and size 7 1/2 shoes. The box was located in Finch's room. This enterprising floor also formed its own Book Club — imagine, while Oprah Winfrey was still a babe in arms. Since budgets allowed only one joint book, a practice of reading aloud was established. I'm told the hallway was packed with pajama-clad enthusiasts, heads pressed tightly together, the night Doherty read from *Peyton Place*, when suddenly she gasped, turned crimson, and ran for her room, where she locked herself in — with Peyton Place. Thus ended the reading for that week.

I lived on "Carrington's Row," named for the Alberta distillers of Rye Whiskey. I don't know who drank that poison, but someone did, because the empties kept turning up, and the handsome bottles beautified rooms up and down the hall. They made excellent containers for our laundry soap. Carrington's Row began life on North Four, and in keeping with the order of hierarchy, moved to the sixth floor in our intermediate year, and finally wound up on the eighth. We never made it to the top of the ladder; two floors still looked down on us to the end of our days. We were never honored with an invitation to Gertrude Hall's inner sanctum, although she did occasionally extend that privilege to those who shared her tenth floor.

Collver remembers parading through Miss Hall's bedroom with a group of classmates the night of the grad dance, an occasion Miss Hall looked forward to with as much relish as her charges. Unfortunately, this year she was confined to bed with a nasty case of shingles, and her attending colleagues were desperately seeking ways to ease her pain and lift her spirits. Someone recognized that a visit from the students could be the perfect medicine, and so "Gertrude's girls" were summoned to make a house call on their way to the dance. The string of radiant young women before her, looking mature and full of promise in their finery, was therapeutic indeed. As they filed past her bed, Miss Hall beamed with pleasure, well pleased with her role in creating such perfection.

Moving "upward" each year was chaotic, as we gathered armloads of belongings and trekked the stairs to our new digs. Telford remembers receiving her order to move from floor seven to floor nine on the very day she'd been granted a late leave for a long-planned special date. She wasn't about to let moving day stand in her way. She'd go on the date, stay out as long as the law allowed, and deal with the move tomorrow.

She returned to her room at midnight, to find it stripped clean, except for the furniture. Where was she? Had someone changed the room number on her door? Maybe she had gotten off the elevator on the wrong floor. She doubled back to check this possibility. No, this was definitely her room. But where were her belongings, and what was she going to do about this dilemma at this hour of the night? She didn't relish the thought of sleeping in her best clothes on a bare mattress. Finally, in desperation, she hiked up the back stairs to the ninth floor to check her newly assigned room.

She inched opened the door gingerly, unsure of who or what she'd find on the other side. She couldn't believe her eyes: there were all her own belongings, just as she had left them two floors below — every last item precisely placed in its allocated drawer, closet or shelf. When she looks back, the name of her date who took priority that night escapes her entirely, but she can name the mystery movers, in spite of their intended anonymity. Telford has been forever grateful for the charitable act of her floor mates, and I am comforted to learn that every home invasion of the time was not an act of savagery.

In-house Dating Service

We were remarkably civilized when it came to dating, and in fact, we developed a very effective dating service, pairing up one another with brothers, cousins, ex-boyfriends or surplus boyfriends. Some classmates had little use for the service, however. They were the girls who had established steady relationships in high school that endured throughout our student nursing days, and concluded at the altar following graduation. (I wonder if they know what they missed?) In any event, there never seemed to be a shortage of guys, since those on the prowl knew exactly where to find a supply of single girls. Our school dances were overrun with guys.

Dating, however, was an exercise in time management, given the hours we worked and the miserly rationing of precious "late leaves." But classmates came to the rescue here, too, sneaking their buddies into residence after curfew through the tunnel door leading from the hospital, or taking the necessary steps to cover for a delinquent classmate out on the town without permission.

Morgan, infamous for having privileges withdrawn for one felony or another, had an ally in D. Miller across the hall, who would stuff Morgan's bed with her teddy bear for her all-night illegal escapades, then in the morning, remove it and make the bed. Fortunately, it didn't take a very big teddy to qualify as a body double for Morgan. And it's amazing how one so small held the distinction of being Carrington Row's resident rebel, constantly railing against authority by doing weird stuff like sneaking into the sunken lounge after hours to play the grand piano in her see-through baby doll pyjamas. That pretty much broke all the rules in one act. Morgan still fumes at the system we were forced to endure, considering it abusive and indicative of the value society placed on women at the time.

I don't know that Murray ever had trouble acquiring a date, but she did have trouble pulling herself together for such an occasion. And I'd wager her recurring pre-date problem was unique. She had a dental plate that carried one tooth — top left front — a replacement for the one knocked out by a crack-the-whip skating accident two years prior at her hometown rink in High River. It was her habit to soak her tooth in a cup while she took her shower and got herself glammed up for a night on the town. The tooth was always the last item in her prep order; she'd pop it into her mouth after blotting her lipstick, then she and her dazzling smile would be good to go. Except the tooth would be missing. "Who thtole my tooth?" we'd hear her cry up and down the hall. She's still asking, and to date, no one's confessed. (I'd put my money on McCullagh, though.)

There seemed to be a bit of a grey area about dating patients, yet it took place openly without consequence, and several classmate found their life partners this way. One particular classmate remembers caring for a patient who couldn't believe his good fortune, surrounded as he was by all these angels of mercy. He and his two brothers lived on a farm, a lifestyle that presented a challenge when it came to crossing paths with girls. A case of appendicitis was a golden opportunity he wasn't about to let slip through his fingers. "How would you and two of your classmates like to go on the town with three handsome farmers?" he proposed to his favorite nurse. Bursting with excitement, she ran the proposition back to her friend Langford in residence. "Sure, I'm game," agreed Langford, "but I get the tallest one." At six feet tall, finding a date she could look up to was always a challenge for Langford, so her demand was agreed upon without dispute. Well, the tallest one turned out to be six foot four, and it wasn't long before Langford gazed up into his eyes at the altar.

Prior to marriage, Langford remembers returning from a trip to

Lethbridge with the "tallest one," arriving a full one and a half hours past her permitted deadline. She was confronted by Mrs. Sanders, leaning back in her chair with a "what's your excuse tonight" look. Thinking fast, Langford invented a tale that was taller than her date. "Mrs. Sanders, you won't believe this, but we hit a porcupine on the highway, and it caused <u>two</u> flat tires!" She was right; Mrs. Sanders didn't for a minute believe. But since the gentle giant had stolen her heart, too, she gave Langford a conspiratorial wink, and waved her off to bed. The tall tale of the prickled tires no doubt entered residence lore as the most outrageous alibi ever.

The last big senior formal dance holds one particularly vivid memory for P. Miller. She recalls that someone arranged a blind date for the evening for Stutz, a fun-loving character who resided on her floor. Stutz was in a dither for days leading up to the momentous occasion, and all eyes were on her as she prepared for the rendezvous. The entire floor was drawn into the affair, and when Stutz's buzzer signalled her date's arrival, heads popped from every room as she scurried down the hall. The silence was deafening as everyone held their breath until she disappeared from sight. The elevator doors had no sooner closed behind her than they popped open again. She was back.

"He's all wrong," she howled, stomping down the hall with her familiar dramatic flair. "You should see the dreadful tie he has on... and that suit!"

"Oh, c'mon, Stutz," everyone chimed in, "forget the suit, what's *he* like?"

"He's got the funniest hair I've ever seen," she wailed, ignoring the issue entirely, as she expounded on the folly of the evening. "I never should have agreed to do this."

"But you haven't given the poor guy a fighting chance," someone argued. "Surely he has one redeeming feature."

"No, he hasn't. He's so-o serious," she complained. "He's a regular geek."

It was setting up to be a long night. It was indeed a long night — long enough for Stutz to do a second appraisal — one that revealed qualities in this young man that she had carelessly dismissed at first glance. She married the geek with the funny hair within months, and they lived happily ever after.

A Creative House

We tried to manage a life beyond studying and room-wrecking, but it took some orchestrating, in view of our long hours of weekday, weekend and shift work. Our schedule made participation in competitive sports a challenge to say the least. I remember turning up for basketball practice with a different circle of team mates every week. Coaching us must have been a nightmare, and facing the polished, organized teams from Tech and U of A, Calgary Branch was daunting. I don't remember ever winning a game, but I'm hoping that it's just my faulty memory talking. We did have successes at baseball games, curling bonspiels and swim meets which took place on a level playing field with the Holy Cross nursing students. Blue ribbons curled up in D. Miller's scrapbook are living proof that she carried the banner for CGH in the pool.

We fairly shone when it came to our stage performances, whether a tea and fashion show — *Hawaiian Holiday* — performed to a packed house, with proceeds paying for the senior class pins, or *'59 Follies*, a standing-room-only production that brought in a monumental $159.00. *Follies* funds were directed toward a class project: the formation of a Diversional Therapy unit, geared toward long term patients on Orthopedics. Our stoic *Can Can* dancers suffered stinging legs for weeks from the coating of shoe polish applied at the dictate of Gertrude Hall. Apparently a dress rehearsal had revealed a far too risqué line of legs glaring beneath the bright lights. Shoe polish, it was decided, could tone down the legs while fitting the budget.

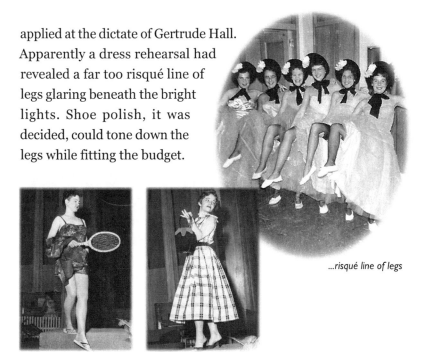

...risqué line of legs

Hawaiian Holiday Models

And finally, our staging of *The Pajama Game* would have been the envy of Broadway. Fraser is still tapping a toe to the memory of:

> Seven and a half cents doesn't buy a hell of a lot
> Seven and a half cents doesn't mean a thing
> But give it to me every hour
> Forty hours every week
> That's enough for me to be living like a king

And show business is show business, whether on Broadway today or in a nursing school auditorium half a century ago. According to local gossip, two members of the chorus line had been eyeing the same dashing member of the audience.

Can Can photo: courtesy Darlene Powell

The nearby Calgary Zoo was a favorite venue for sunny day walks, wiener roasts, death defying swims in the fast-flowing, frigid Bow River, and the traditional closing ceremony at which we shredded our blue-check dresses and fed them into a blazing bonfire — a ritual officially known as *The Burning of the Blues.*

The Burning of the Blues

In the end, though, I think we would all agree with Zelenka's recently voiced sentiment. "My favorite memories of residence life are the long conversations we used to have in the hall in our PJs." Amen to our own pajama game.

Blues photo: courtesy Edith Schroeder
PJs photo: courtesy Darlene Powell

Chapter 3

– THE SCHOOL –

"To her, I was no doubt one more blob of adolescent clay to be molded into a woman capable of moving quietly, thinking carefully and acting wisely. Not an easy task ahead of her. She must have known I was not equipped to take in my hands the guiding of birth, death and human destiny — or even of myself."

Susan Bates, student nurse, on her superintendent —
— *A Lamp is Heavy*, 1950, Sheila Mackay Russell (Mackay, Class of '42).

Labor Trumps Learning

Throughout the first half century in the history of the Calgary General Hospital School of Nursing, student nurses received supervised on-the-job training, but their role as indispensable members of the labor force always took priority over their learning experience. And *labor* was the operative word; nurses performed almost every domestic task — cleaning, laundry, cooking, maintenance — as well as bedside care, while anything of a *medical* nature, such as taking blood pressures or administering injections, remained in the educated hands of the doctor. Hospitals had little difficulty recruiting women for their training programs, especially during the depression years when it was often the only viable option for struggling parents desiring to educate their daughters. Farm girls were especially drawn to an opportunity to escape the drudgery of their drought-ravaged homesteads.

When the Second World War broke out, graduate nurses willingly answered the call to serve, leaving hospitals on the home front with a grave shortage. Now, more than ever, the student nurse carried the workload for her hospital. Yet this was a model that would continue well into the post-war reconstruction period. Hospitals neglected to differentiate between supplying a good nursing service and developing a good educational system in its school; the student's educational needs were inevitably secondary to the hospital's service needs.

In 1947, Alberta's Social Credit government announced a resolution to guarantee stable staffing in each of its ten large hospitals by increasing enrolment in its nurse-training programs. Yet two circumstances of the time would make this difficult to achieve: More post-secondary educational options were beginning to open up for women, and a burgeoning post-war marriage rate meant that many were opting for motherhood and homemaking. And so, the government took a step backward to draw recruits; it lowered admission requirements to its training schools — ironically, just when better educated and more skilled nurses were needed. Medical and surgical treatments were becoming increasingly complex, and procedures once confined to the doctor's expertise, were now assigned to the nurse. The student nurse needed to learn these skills, and the repetitive, mundane tasks of filling water jugs, delivering lab specimens, tending flowers, and listing all the personal effects of every patient on admission, did not contribute to her education.

Sheila Mackay Russell, valedictorian for the Class of '42, lamented, "the same twelve-hour shifts, the same burden of menial tasks, the same attitude of students paying for their training with labor," adding forlornly, "and the scales tip in favor of labor." In her time-honored novel, *A Lamp Is Heavy*, Russell does not conceal her admiration for the intelligent, strong Jessie Connal and her selfless contemporaries who sacrificed personal lives for dedication to service, yet knew the need for change was overdue. She was not alone.

Crisis Brings Change

By 1951, the Calgary General Hospital was in crisis: Anne Hebert had resigned after ten years as Superintendent of Nurses; graduate nurses were frequently assigned the same housekeeping duties as domestic personnel, and in some instances, paid less; generally poor working conditions were causing a high turnover of graduate nurses; and shift rotation and days off schedules were not maintained for nursing staff. Pleas from the Alberta Association of Registered Nurses (AARN) for regular and consistent inspection of hospital nurse-training programs had been declined. Standards were virtually non-existent. Cries for improved conditions fell on deaf ears, and things continued to deteriorate. Finally, with morale at rock bottom, Eileen Jameson (Class of '45) formed a staff Nurses' Association, "to give strength and unity" to the nurses' drive for change.

On January 14, 1952, eighty-two (out of 85) graduate nurses delivered a four-page letter through a lawyer to the hospital's board of trustees, threatening to resign en masse by the last day of February, 1952 unless "immediate steps are taken to implement our recommendations." Faced with open rebellion, the Board acted. It commissioned Miss H. M. Lamont, Superintendent of Nurses of Montreal's Royal Victoria Hospital, to conduct a survey to evaluate staff requests. Her report came as no surprise.

Miss Lamont confirmed a number of realities: that organization in the nursing department was poor; that there was a lack of coordination between medical staff and administration, making it impossible for the acting Superintendent of Nurses to present nursing problems for resolution; that the school curriculum had little relevance to modern educational practices, and there was no overall plan of study (student rotation was poor, frequently creating a situation where students received clinical experience without prerequisite instruction); and as always, that clinical experience was frequently interrupted to meet nursing service needs. Furthermore, Miss Lamont strongly suggested that the physical plant of the hospital, with its outmoded facilities and lack of space, was altogether inadequate.

Finally, Miss Lamont insisted that successful changes could only be achieved through the appointment of a new, qualified Director of Nursing. Her recommendations led to three major eventualities: a resolution to build an entirely new facility; the recruitment of Dr. L. O. Bradley, formerly Executive Secretary of the Canadian Hospital Council, as Administrator; and the advent of Gertrude Hall, who replaced acting Superintendent of Nurses, Margaret Macdonald (Class of '26), our "Black Mac."

Gertrude May Hall

On a crisp October day in 1952, Gertrude May Hall, age fifty-five, with thirty-six continuous years of nursing service to her credit, swept into the Calgary General Hospital at the calling of its forward-thinking administrator, Dr. L. O. Bradley. The hospital still faced a year of construction, but Gertrude Hall began "sweeping" the first day, and never stopped. An experienced and dedicated nurse, she was a woman on a mission. The Calgary General's reputation had been faltering for years, and both its medical team and the city fathers counted on their new director to develop a plan that would restore its honor in the eyes of the country. Experience told Gertrude Hall that the success of any hospital hinges on the stature of its nurses, and top quality nurses can only be achieved through top quality teaching.

And so sweeping changes were made in the nursing school, in keeping with Gertrude Hall's fundamental philosophy that the student nurse's clinical rotations must be designed to meet that student's learning needs, not the service needs of the hospital. She pushed for the use of auxiliary personnel to free graduate and student nurses from repetitive domestic tasks, and she pushed for adequate funding for the hospital to meet its primary purpose of providing care for the sick, but she *demanded* top drawer education, without compromise, for her students. Under her watch, student education and patient care were now viewed as separate entities; staffing needs would never be allowed to jeopardize the student's education experience. I would learn the seriousness of Miss Hall's intentions firsthand with my first personal encounter.

I was manning the desk on my assigned surgical ward when the phone rang. I lifted the receiver to the frantic voice of West Five's head nurse seeking staffing assistance. Miss Hall, coincidentally at my side, overheard the conversation and reached for the phone.

"Hello. Gertrude Hall here..."

"Oh! Miss Hall, we're desperately short-staffed today," came the desperate cry, "I've lost one graduate and two students to the flu this shift. Can you send me a student from East Three to give us a hand?"

I was already rising, fully expecting Miss Hall to send me running. Her surprise response dropped me back into my chair.

"Absolutely not," was her impatient — if not edgy — reply, "my students are here for their surgical experience, and they can't get that on West Five."

Only when she was assured that her message was understood

once and for all, did she proceed to address the plight at hand with an alternative solution. Only now, all these years later, have I fully grasped my providential timing — my good fortune to pass through the Calgary General Hospital's School of Nursing during the crucial years of this remarkable woman's eight-year tenure.

Margaret C. M. Street

To meet her lofty goals, Miss Hall hired Margaret C. M. Street, as her Associate Director of Nursing, assigning her the monumental task of drawing up a master plan for every student in the school, a plan that would co-ordinate our classroom lectures with our clinical experience. I can still see that enormous chart spreading across Miss Street's office wall, displaying our every assignment for our entire three years. Once again, we only recognized the merit of our master plan education belatedly through the envious comments of nursing graduates from other schools. Miss Street also won our admiration as President of the AARN during her time with us (1957) and for taking driving lessons at her advanced age. Imagine!

Margaret Street's plan was only workable for one class enrolment per year, so the customary spring class was eliminated from the curriculum in favor of one fall class. The Class of '56 was the first "fall only" class, and the first to receive their entire education under the design of Margaret Street and Gertrude Hall. There were many "firsts" for this class, and at their graduation exercises, Mayor Don Mackay acknowledged Gertrude Hall's achievement in their superior education, by proclaiming that henceforth, the school would be known as the *Gertrude M. Hall School of Nursing*.

However, Mackay's impulse designation must have met with resistance — possibly from alumnae bent on preserving its history — because it was never officially adopted. Unofficially, the name was assumed in the minds of many graduates from that era; the *Calgary General Hospital School of Nursing* and *Gertrude M. Hall* are invariably spoken in the same breath.

Finally, R. Catherine Aikin was hired as Associate Director of Nursing Education in direct charge of the nursing school, making up the final member of the team. Miss Aikin's steel trap mind not only locked in our names after one encounter, but I'd bet my boots she could have recited everyone's grades in every subject at the drop of a cap. Those who didn't measure up to her criteria at the end of our junior study block were out the door. About twenty classmates didn't survive that first year, although not all casualties were due to low grades; some made the enlightening discovery that they were simply not cut out to be nurses. LaGrandeur confesses she wavered for a time, when she noted that all three of our directors and an overwhelming number of our instructors were single.

R. Catherine Aikin

The first classes under Gertrude Hall's reign were the lucky beneficiaries of the eight-hour day, which must have seemed a luxury to all the sisters who had slaved through twelve-hour days before us. Gone, too, were the six and a half day weeks; we worked a mere six days a week with a half day off for statutory holidays. How well I remember plotting a three-day break over New Year's by combining the allotted half day each for Christmas and New Year's with my regular days off for two consecutive weeks. Then I slept the entire three days. So much for a rollicking New Year's Eve... By the time the lucky Class of '61 came along, the 44-hour week was implemented, and one year later, the Class of '62 shared a 40-hour week with the rest if the world. A-h-h, born too soon.

Hands On

Our school, conveniently attached to the residence, was state-of-the-art. One classroom, accommodating sixty students, had elevated seats overlooking a revolving platform so that we could scrutinize every side of Mrs. Chase, the practice dummy, as she endured her morning enema at the hands of our nursing arts instructor. Mrs. Sanborn, her long suffering compatriot, clung to the sheets of the adjacent bed awaiting her turn.

Science Lab

In addition to a fully equipped science lab and a well stocked library, there were three smaller classrooms that boasted darkening drapes for movies or slides and x-ray view boxes. But most noteworthy were the thirteen-bed practice rooms equipped to replicate actual hospital wards, with linen carts, service room, chart room and kitchenette. Here Mrs. Chase suffered our unskilled hands-on sessions of bed baths, back rubs, sheet-changing and more encounters with the bedpan than she could possibly require in spite of her morning enema. I might add, however, that Mrs. Chase was not the only one to suffer the consequences of our clumsy hands; we were frequently at the mercy of a fellow classmate practicing the lesson of the day on us, although we drew the line at the enema.

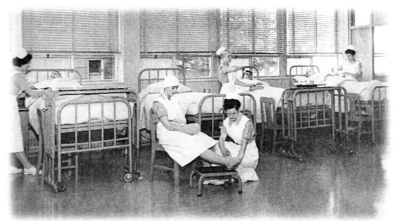

Practice Room

Then, too, there was the period in our second year when the practice rooms were hastily pressed into active duty. No more practising; this was the real McCoy. The Asian flu hit town with a vengeance, and students were struck down en masse, quickly overflowing the hospital infirmary. Overnight, classmates went from honing their skills at making beds, to crawling into them, as the practice room became their sick bay. I was one of the lucky ones to escape the virus, and my memory is of rolling carts of fluids through the tunnel for my feverish classmates, on my return to residence from regular hospital duties. Hospital staff were also taken down, so that an impossible workload was created for those of us left standing. There were times, in our exhaustion, when we guiltily wondered whether succumbing to the virus wasn't preferable to eluding it.

Thiessen remembers being the first one admitted to the practice room, and reports how terribly ill she was. She recalls one classmate in a nearby bed who suffered only a mild case of the flu — a blessing for her, but a nightmare for the rest of them. The happy victim chatted up a storm, denying everyone else a minute's peace or any longed-for sleep. Someone eventually pleaded with the medication nurse to give Chatty Cathy a sedative. She obliged, and everyone enjoyed a blissful night's sleep. Their anesthetised friend slept all the next day.

About a year prior to the flu scourge, the same practice room was the setting for another event: a classmate practising a preoperative shave prep on Thiessen's legs. In that era, not all young women shaved their legs as a regular grooming habit, and Thiessen admits she's still having a hard time forgiving that classmate. "I have had to shave these legs ever since," she moans. And that led her to thoughts of another lifetime adjustment she's had to make, all in the name of being the sacrificial lamb for a sister.

"I was stupid enough to volunteer to be a patient the day we were learning to pass down gastric tubes," Thiessen recalls all too vividly. After Thiessen had endured the nightmare of gagging and retching throughout the insertion of the tube into the stomach, the instructor arrived to demonstrate the method for withdrawing fluid and testing for acidity. Before Thiessen could gain her composure, a clumsy practice session was turning into a medical crisis; the test revealed a lack of acid, and an alarmed instructor was shipping the stomach contents off to the hospital lab for more in-depth study. Just when Thiessen was thanking her lucky stars she'd never have to endure this nasty procedure again, the Student Health Office scheduled a follow-up repeat... on a cherished day off, if you please.

The dreaded GI tube went down with less effort in the hands of an expert, but unfortunately the acid analysis remained consistent with that of the practice test. After an initial stab at HCl tablets that resulted in burning stomach pangs, followed by years of doctors largely ignoring the situation, Thiessen finally landed a doctor in the 1980s who fully understood the consequences of low stomach acid — improper absorption of Vitamin B12. She now enjoys excellent health administering her own B12 injections. Every encounter with the gastroscope to monitor her situation carries her back to that tube day in the practice room so long ago.

The number of classmates who have related memories of gagging on that frightful GI tube should send me on a major guilt trip for the role I secured on the delivery end of things, but having been raised by a mother who preached that "it is more blessed to give than to receive," what was I to do? I remember practising my skills on Collver, who was a model patient, breathing and swallowing in synch with my inching the tube down her esophagus. We executed the procedure with astonishing precision — not one life-threatening gag — and in record time. Then just as I summoned the instructor to claim bragging rights, Collver suddenly, and inexplicably, grabbed the end of that tube, and in one swift motion, yanked it out as though cracking a whip... with absolutely no regard for her diligent, dedicated, flabbergasted partner. Then without a shred of guilt, she shrugged her shoulders and gave me a, "yeah, well you try it" look. For anyone wondering where the expression "up your nose with a rubber hose" comes from, I think I have the answer. In any event,

Collver received no quibble from a partner too smart to risk the
possibility of role reversal.

On another occasion Collver and I found ourselves back in the
practice room together. This time, it was in the evening, and we were
practising bed-making — working on getting those mitred corners
just so. But it was casual, unsupervised time, so the atmosphere was
relaxed and jovial. Then, in an instant, life got serious. For Collver,
it would never be the same. I have granted her request to tell the
story in her own words:

> Late November, 1956. The evening. For some reason, I was
> in the nursing school, along with some other classmates. We were
> practising something — it might have been making beds. I was
> called to the residence office. There I found Birdie Finch. She told
> me that it was necessary for me to go to the emergency ward, and
> she would accompany me. I was young, and naive enough that I
> went along with no apprehension.
>
> We walked through the tunnel together, and to her credit
> she said nothing of the reason for my being summoned. When we
> arrived at the desk in the old emergency ward, I saw a neighbour
> and her son sitting in the waiting room. I spoke to them, but still
> did not sense that anything was amiss. Then I heard the doctor
> speaking on the phone — "Jim (Francis, our family doctor), we
> have a Judy Collver here, DOA. Could you come and identify her?"
> I remember that my knees gave way, and I found myself on the
> floor. My sister. He was speaking of my sister. She was only fifteen
> years old.
>
> Mom and Dad came out from a side room where they had
> been waiting for me. The remainder of that evening was a blur.
> We drove home, and a neighbour came across the lawn to meet
> us. I remember Dad saying, "She's gone, Dode." Somehow, we
> all found ourselves in our home, with a cup of tea being served.

Dr. Francis appeared at our front door, bringing with him kindness and sleeping pills to help us find some rest that night. Our dear neighbour — I'm sure that she was in and out of our home many times after that fateful day — bringing food, making tea, bringing herself into our lives, while we spoke and visited with friends who had heard of Judy's death.

Judy had been passionately fond of horses, and was a regular visitor at the barns on the Stampede grounds. She had a lot of knowledge about horse racing, race horses and jockeys. Denny Layzell wrote a piece about her in his column in *The Calgary Herald*, the writer, a lover of horses himself. He contended that followers of thoroughbreds go to a special place he referred to as *Cloud Eight*. "We know a lot of wonderful people there who will be Judy's friends," he assured the reader. "God bless her."

Her death, as does any ending of life, altered our lives in a way that we had never dreamed of. Since there were only two of us, I felt very alone after her passing. And there have been many times since that day when I have thought, "Wouldn't it be good if Judy was here?" She was the aunt that my children never knew. She was the child who never reached her full potential. We will never know why these things happen. They just do.

Does it still hurt to speak of her? In all honesty, I believe that I can answer no. The memories are there, but, for the most part, the pain is not. There are still times, though, when I think, "I wish Judy was here."

Nearing the end of our training days, another classmate would also experience the unimaginable loss of a young sibling. On her arrival at residence from ward duty one June day, LaGrandeur received word to call home to Windermere, B.C. The news her mother delivered was shattering: her beloved brother Monty, age twenty, had been killed in a car accident. Monty had been especially close to his sister, often dropping into the nurses' residence to say hi because he missed her so. LaGrandeur recalls running down the hall for the phone to learn that Monty was waiting in the lobby. That always brought a ready smile to her face. Then, in the flash of skidding tires on a highway, it was over. No more cheering visits. No more Monty hugs in the lobby. Only a heart full of memories.

I remember feeling ill-equipped to bring comfort to these classmates through their suffering. At that young age, I lacked the life experiences that prepare a person for such situations, but in addition, it was a time when death and grief were rarely discussed openly... even in hospitals. We were all ill-equipped, and the School of Nursing was no exception. I'm sure it fell short in bringing solace to these girls. Miss Aikin spent an hour or so with Collver, for which she was grateful, and Miss Street offered formal condolences from the school to LaGrandeur, but the School allowed little bereavement time as it subtly conveyed its expectation of "duty first." "It was a different time," LaGrandeur says today, looking back with understanding, "and people were expected to just 'buck up' and get on with life."

Elisabeth Kübler-Ross's groundbreaking work with the dying in the sixties brought radical changes to our attitudes. Her clear understanding and uninhibited acceptance of death opened the doors to candid dialogue with the dying and the bereaved. The end result is the awe-inspiring care offered by the hospices of today.

McElheran remembers her first experience with death, that of a patient on West Five — a "before Kübler-Ross" experience. It was an elderly woman, whose husband clung to her hand, desperately willing her to live. On witnessing her last breath, the distraught man threw himself onto the bed, sobbing uncontrollably as he embraced his lifeless partner. McElheran, traumatized by the unfamiliar, disturbing scene, spontaneously burst into tears herself. The attending clinical instructor promptly steered her charge down the hall to the service room.

"You must never display such a show of empathy," she scolded, embracing her old-school philosophy. "You will learn to control your feelings in front of patients and family members."

Fortunately, McElheran's inherent compassion for others stood in the way of her complying fully to the instructor's dictate. And she is able to smile at the memory of a later encounter with death. She arrived for duty on West Six one morning to learn in report that Mr. Hamlet had died in the night, and the head nurse was suggesting, "this would be a good opportunity for students to observe the preparation of a body for the morgue." So McElheran followed the orderly into the "quiet room" where he performed the entire procedure reciting Shakespeare.

Zelenka's morgue experience was a far cry from that. She returned to residence from class one afternoon wide-eyed and jabbering a blue streak about the day's lesson: how to prepare a body for the morgue. She was so caught up in the drama of the exercise, we decided a practice run was in order, and she should be our dummy corpse. Giggling with enthusiasm, she offered herself up without hesitation. So we set about swaddling her in sheets from head to toe (far more than instructions called for), until she looked like an Egyptian mummy. Then, of course, we hated to waste such a work of art, and since we had no access to the morgue, we rolled our corpse onto the residence elevator, and sent it up to the 10th floor... with stops at every floor along the way. Unholy screams rang down that elevator shaft as the doors glided open on each floor to reveal a misplaced, motionless body in a scene snatched from *Night of the Living Dead*. Zelenka gasped for air as she carefully counted stops to the top: seven... eight... nine... ten, where she gave up the ghost, convinced Gertrude Hall would step on board, and God only knew what would happen then. To this day, the architects of this affair regret that Gertrude failed to show. She missed some impressive handiwork, and not even God got to find out what would happen then.

We all remember our first injection, which we could only administer to a real person after we'd perfected the procedure — with meticulous sterile technique — on an orange. We drew the line at offering ourselves up as volunteers for this exercise, instead annihilating an orchard of oranges before declaring ourselves to be armed and ready.

Neufeld remembers Miss Fallis, her East Four surgical instructor, running through a final dress rehearsal outside the room of a hapless patient, before waving Neufeld inside for her premiere performance. With one hand still on the door, Miss Fallis whispered a final word of caution, "Whatever you do, don't tell Mr. Poke that you're a new student, or that this is your first injection. He doesn't need to know that." And so Neufeld, weapon in hand, and wearing a false smile of confidence as she harbored her secret, strode into the room with every intention of handling this situation like a pro.

As she approached the bed, Miss Fallis rushed past her to the patient's side, and patting him soothingly on the arm, divulged sympathetically, "Now this is my little nurse's first injection, but just relax and everything will be fine." After receiving his penicillin shot, the patient, having been programmed for a flawed execution, responded as one might expect: "That hurt way more than usual." He turned to Miss Fallis for solace, and got another tender pat on the arm.

Fraser remembers Miss Fallis leading her group of students on their introductory tour of East Four, starting in the service room where she announced, "This is a cupboard," and pointed out the familiar item mounted on the wall. They awaited further elaboration, but it didn't come. Did she lose her train of thought, they wondered, or did she think they didn't know a cupboard when they saw one? I'm suspecting this was her quirky sense of humor at work. We nicknamed Miss Fallis "Folly Dolly," but I can't remember why. Tigner mentioned in a passing communication that she only remembers one clinical instructor out of the entire slate; she describes her as "lovely and pleasantly confused much of the time." I have no idea who she's talking about.

We had a procedure manual — our green book — that listed everything from the rudimentary task of manoeuvring a bedpan to the more advanced exercises of suctioning tracheotomies or assisting doctors with spinal taps. Every procedure, even the handling of the common bedpan, was a terrifying, complicated affair for the first-time junior student, and panic could freeze the brain at the worst of times. I doubt that Finch was the first or the last to slide a bedpan front to back under her hapless patient, but I sincerely hope Dingwall was the first *and* the last to insert a pan upside down.

The "Green Book"

Unfortunately, the manual did not forewarn us of possible misadventures in the service room. Beers would have welcomed a reminder to always secure the hopper door before stepping on the flusher — creating Mount Vesuvius in a closet. The tunnel seemed ten miles long the day she experienced that accident, as she trekked back to residence to peel off her soggy uniform, take a shower, and begin her day again. She didn't ask who cleaned up the service room.

No manual on earth would think to address the episode Zelenka experienced in the service room one day. I'd bet the farm it was unique in the history of the Calgary General Hospital. The story goes, Zelenka was bending over the hopper absorbed in yet another bedpan flush and swish routine, when Zoeteman arrived bearing a pan requiring the same attention. With no time to wait for the hopper, Zoeteman decided she'd park the pan and attend to it later. She quickly sized up the perfect shelf to serve her purpose; she plunked her pan on Zelenka's back, and fled. Zelenka is not too clear on the conclusion of this story — it seems she's repressed it — but we do know an unwritten rule was enforced from that day on: "Only one 'Z' allowed in the service room at a time."

Dingwall chuckles today as she recounts her surprise in the service room fifty years ago. It began as an average day with a manageable patient load, but there was one stumbling block — one particular patient was creating tension. He was a kind, co-operative patient, but he had also been her high school principal, and she felt awkward with this new, unfamiliar relationship. She had never particularly relished the task of collecting a patient's dental plates for cleaning, but asking her high school principal to deposit his teeth in a kidney basin bordered on unthinkable. However, she faced up to it, and so did he, and off she went to scrub up his "Colgate" smile. When she got to the sink, however, she discovered an unexpected object staring at her from the basin — his glass eyeball awaited its turn for a bath.

The morning bed bath, though routine, was an elaborate affair that the nurse was to carry out face to foot with precision, tucking the flannel bath sheet under each separate limb as the bath progressed. It concluded with a soothing wash and vigorous rub of the back, which brought the patient a great sense of well being. Whatever has happened to the irreplaceable back rub? The morning bath was also a time for nurse and patient to build a relationship, an important component to the healing process. Of course, if you're a junior student and your patient is the associate director, Margaret Street, relating and healing are not foremost in your thoughts. Even today, Hill is scarcely able to relate her experience in this very scenario without suffering an anxiety attack or an outbreak of hives. At the time, she was absolutely certain she was going to omit some crucial step in Miss Street's bath routine and it would all end right there — she'd be out the door. Whether her rattled brain remembered to dry Miss Street's feet — both of them — is open to conjecture, but we do know that both women lived to see another day.

Bedmaking was almost as complex as the bed bath, and carried its own precise order of things: clean linens on this side, soiled ones on that side; a pleat in the foot of the top sheet to allow movement of the feet; square corners when tucking in the sides; open end of the pillow cases facing away from the door; likewise, towels hung with open ends away from the door; castors on the bed turned in. We were never allowed to place the bedpan on the over-the-bed table. (I still hang my bathroom towels with the open ends away from the door in my home today. My children call it anal. What do they know about anal?) Lastly, one dare not forget the final item — one of utmost importance — the newspaper waste bag that had to be pinned to the mattress. Transforming used newspapers into bags called for highly skilled labor. We were earth-friendly recyclers half a century before our time.

McKenzie has never forgotten the morning she had completed every step of her bath and bedmaking assignment to perfection, only to receive a dressing down from the instructor for leaving the window open. She's also not forgotten her sympathetic patient who was quick to jump to her defence with the false claim that the window was open at her request. "I remember many patients who rallied for us," noted McKenzie, "when they witnessed the pickiness of some of our instructors." Of course, not every patient was so inclined, as Finch can attest.

It was a particularly backbreaking morning, and her last assigned patient was an extremely obese woman, who was regrettably powerless to roll onto her side so that Finch could remove the bottom sheet. Desperate to complete her mission before the dreaded instructor turned up for inspection, she had gone from one side of the bed to the other, pushing, prodding and pleading with Mrs. Poly to roll over, but there was no budging her. Finally, in her exhausted state, there was only one thing left for Finch to do; she pulled the footstool out from under the bed, sat on it, and bawled her head off. A puzzled Mrs. Poly peered over the side of her bed, perplexed at the sight of this hopeless nurse sobbing below.

Fraser looks back with fond respect for Nancy White, whom she viewed as a *thinking* instructor — a trait that perhaps set her apart. Miss White oversaw the students on orthopedics, a specialty in which Fraser felt way over her head most of the time as a junior student. Struggling to maintain balance with everything expected of her, she was relieved — and impressed — when Miss White preached, "Don't worry about the bed castors; just give good care to your patients." Today Fraser claims, "Nancy White was probably the main reason I stuck it out."

The last of the books was the Blue Book, which listed all the procedures we were expected to perform at a respectable skill level, and within our allotted three years. Our clinical instructors had the responsibility of supervising our performances and signing confirmation of their witnessing. As we headed down the home stretch of our third year, we had to pay close attention to the procedures we had not yet executed. Some instructors took particular interest in helping us complete our Blue Books by keeping an eye out for opportunities to give us certain experience. Perhaps they might even re-assign patients to help us meet a requirement. One instructor, on the other hand , covertly assisted a classmate in the evasion of an experience. Tigner still lives with guilt for coercing that instructor (surely not the pleasantly confused one) into the illicit act of signing off "irrigation of a colostomy" in her Blue Book, a procedure Tigner simply could not bring herself to execute.

Dressing for the Job

From day one, we attended all classes in full uniform, the same as required for ward duty: blue check dresses under white bibs and aprons, with white shoes and stockings, and caps. Our functional, short-sleeved dresses with self collars and cuffs were conceived by the practical Gertrude Hall in a once-and-for-all answer to a progression of changes through the years from long to short sleeves, both trimmed with encumbering, stiffly-starched, detachable collars and cuffs. Footwear began with black hi-topped boots, which eventually gave way to the lower cut black oxford, and finally, the more complementary white shoe. Stockings moved from black to white with their corresponding shoe color. The Class of '56 was the first to wear the blue checks for all three years, although for the first year they remained in the unflattering black shoes and stockings, and they received caps only after completing their six-month probationary period. The Class of '57 pioneered the wearing of caps with white shoes and stockings from day one, much to the chagrin of their big sisters.

Students from the pre-Gertrude Hall era hold fond memories of the time-honored capping ceremony, having embraced it as a noteworthy stepping stone in their first year. The school's new director, however, had different designs regarding the affair. Her first move was to scale the ceremony down significantly, beginning with its invitation list, which would now exclude parents. The first recipients of the modification were members of the Class of '56, a no-nonsense band of rebels who were incensed over this intolerable circumstance. They quickly rallied forces, and drew up a petition that demanded the inclusion of parents at their much anticipated ceremony. They boldly presented it to Gertrude Hall, smugly confident that they'd win their rightful due. Such folly! They learned in a flash that a petition held utterly no clout with Gertrude Hall, who swiftly countered with a clear, strong reminder of just who was in charge. One year later, the capping ceremony was silently removed from the school's event calendar without fanfare. Yet, ceremony or not, the cap and its status-signifying band retained its standing throughout the life of the school.

Black band of a graduate

As junior students, we wore caps with no bands, so it was a big day the following September when we were presented with light blue stripes on becoming intermediates, and eventually, dark blue as seniors. For the most part, our bands went unnoticed by our hospital patients, but we were acutely aware of the status they announced to all medical staff. Would we junior students ever become revered seniors? Needless to say, we walked on air when we were awarded the black band of a graduate.

The bands were made of 5/8" strips of velveteen, which we pinned with straight pins through the thin edge of the cap, allowing it to be removed and re-pinned with each laundering. The band had to be pinned taut enough not to droop down the face of the cap, but too taut would cause the wings to splay like Dumbo's ears. Thiessen remembers her band inevitably heading south every time she encountered Miss Aikin, who was perfection personified. Miss Aikin's military background never allowed a detail such as this to pass her by. "Miss Thiessen," she'd say with a scowl, "your band is slipping."

Finally, after many such encounters, a sympathetic classmate suggested that Thiessen secure her band with a thin piece of tape. The following morning she saw Miss Aikin approaching, and inwardly sighed with relief that her band was smartly in place. "Good morning, Miss Aikin," she glowed with confidence, holding her head erect. "Good morning, Miss Thiessen," came the curt reply, as Miss Aikin scrutinized the edge of the cap. "It is fine to secure your band with tape," she frowned, "but it is not fine for the tape to show." It was nigh impossible to measure up to Kate Aikin's military standards, a fact Thiessen had reinforced time and again.

In the late sixties, the slow death of the cap began. As nursing schools moved toward community college and university settings, the ritualized progression through the ranks of apprenticeship no longer dominated nursing education, and the cap, signifying achievement as the student moved upward through levels, lost much of its symbolic meaning. University and college faculties were therefore the first to dispense with it, although a surprising number of new generation students initially resisted the change; they still viewed the cap as a symbol of their profession. Yet it was always a gender-specific symbol, and nursing leaders encouraging men to enter the profession, began to view this as a conflict — cementing the push to let it go. And so, our noble crown slipped from sight. It is missed by many.

Occasionally, the school allowed us to not wear uniforms to class on a Saturday, in order to allow out-of-town girls time to catch transportation home for a Sunday off. Neufeld, the quiet girl from Didsbury who never stepped out of line, took weeks to work up the courage to wear street clothes to a Saturday class, hoping to fly out the door and down to the bus depot in time for the early bus home.

To her dismay, she was the only one in the entire class in civvies that Saturday, so she felt uncomfortably conspicuous. Miss Aikin's arrival only added to her discomfort. Summoning each girl to come forward individually to collect assignments, she glared sternly at Neufeld, and demanded, "Why are you wearing street clothes today?" "I'm hoping to catch the 4:00 o'clock bus to Didsbury," Neufeld explained timidly. Miss Aikin delayed that Saturday class longer then ever before. Neufeld missed her bus.

A final treasured accessory to our attire was our class pin, designed by our "little sisters," and presented to us when we entered

our third year. We loved this tradition on both sides of the equation — designing a pin for our "big sisters," then a year later, receiving our own pins from the drawing board of our "little sisters." All classes received the standard Calgary General Hospital School of Nursing pin awarded on graduation.

Class of '58 pin: courtesy Barbara Dobbie

The Long Road

Many in our midst entertained, one time or another, the idea of quitting. This was an inevitable response to relentless, crushing fatigue, combined with the strain of life under round-the-clock scrutiny. Fraser claims, "I wanted to quit every day." For some, walking away became a reality, but for those of us determined to tough it out, we found strength and comfort in one another as we plodded the exhausting road together. Of course, we also had cheerleaders outside our walls. For Molyneaux, teetering on the brink of resignation early in the race, her father became a devoted champion, coaxing her to the finish line with one of his celebrated poems, shared in part below:

> Just stick to it Joy, don't let it get you down,
> For a nurse should never wear, a troubled look or frown.
> We are all proud, of the work our daughter has been choosing,
> And never feel that ever, our confidence you're losing.
> Studies may be hard, Joy, and days in wards be tough,
> But never is the road through life, without a little rough.
> When you feel that tests and exams, are all going wrong,
> Just think of the smiles of your patients, when you come along.
> Everyone is pulling, for you to be a real success,
> And looking for the day when you, will wear a full white dress.
> So talk it over with those, who are of settled mind,
> You'll find that all will give advice, that is wise and kind.
> Bring home your problems, and let us help you out,
> We may not be able, but we'll try without a doubt.
> And when the day comes, when we see your graduation,
> Our hearts will share, in our daughter's sure elation.
> So stick it out, Joy, you won't let it get you down,
> You are surely going to be, the finest nurse in town.
>
> -Roy Molyneux

On Wednesday, October 14th, 1959, the Class of '59 — eighty-six of us (the largest class to date) — walked across the stage of our residence auditorium to receive our diplomas. It was official; we were registered nurses. The "RN" initials we could now attach to our names did not designate a degree per se, but a legal title to indicate we had completed a three-year nursing program and passed the standardized exams set down by our professional organization, the Alberta Association of Registered Nurses. The official designation, first awarded in 1919, carried the privileges of our organization, as well as its protection, both to us, and to those under our care.

...walked across the stage of our residence auditorium to receive our diplomas.

Regrettably, we were denied one classmate's presence with us that night, due to her having failed two RN exams. Today she describes graduation day as the darkest day of her life. She persevered, however, by repeating her clinical experience in the areas in question the following year, and with the kind assistance of the two clinical instructors involved, and coaching from two generous classmates, she passed the rewrite exams. She achieved

Photo: courtesy Melinda Price

her dream some months after the rest of us, but there was never a moment when we didn't consider her one of us.

When we arrived for our graduation exercises, we were surprised to find Margaret Street at the helm in place of Gertrude Hall, who was suffering an untimely attack of shingles. The pain of her shingles as she lay in her private room on West Six — my very first assigned ward — no doubt paled in comparison to the agony of missing that long anticipated evening. However, I feel certain that as Miss Street greeted each of us with her warm, motherly smile, Miss Hall eased back into her pillow, and found a measure of relief as she, too, watched each passing face in her mind's eye. Fraser bounced into her room first thing the next morning, brimming with delight that she had graduated after near insurmountable first-year struggles. "Miss Hall, I graduated!" she beamed. Miss Hall returned her smile.

A departure from the blue checks.

Photo: courtesy Edith Schroeder

Beers, our capable Valedictorian, remembers little of her prominent role in the evening's festivities. She recalls that Gertrude Hall worked closely with her on the composition of her speech, and the unfortunate circumstance that Miss Hall was unable to witness her performance. But few are aware of the truly amazing feat Beers performed that night. Moments before she took her place on stage, her boyfriend, attending university in California, had phoned her long distance "person-to-person," an action that at that time was reserved for either the very rich or the recklessly frivolous. He was neither. But he did consider that a proposal of marriage rated, and I dare say it did. The girl said "YES!" and, head dizzy with joy, she stepped up to the podium with the poise of a pro, to deliver a flawless address. Miss Hall would have been proud. We certainly were.

...ready for the world.

The evening was the culmination of three trying but triumphant years together, and now our commiserative, communal life was over. We were confident we had received an exceptional nursing education — one that spanned 1,095 days — but we'd also lived the same number of days under a regime that had dictated our every move. Now, overnight, it was cold-heartedly flinging us from the nest. Could we fly? Well, there may have been the odd nose-dive, but on the whole, we flapped and flew — maybe even soared — proving to ourselves that we were ready for the world. And we won't forget that first pay check that we received as real, honest-to-goodness nurses. After a starting salary of $10.00 per month as students, increasing to $12.50 in our second year, and topping out at $15.00 per month as seniors, we were now in clover, commanding a whopping $249.00 per month, with increments to a maximum of $289.00 monthly over two years. *Well, I've come full circle,* I remember murmuring to myself, as I examined a pay check that matched the last one I had earned as a typist for the Royalite Oil Company three years prior, a position I gave up to enter nursing school. Somehow, though, I felt taller now, and far more worthy.

One year later, the Class of '60 — our little sisters — took the same walk, but the school was not only bidding them farewell; it was also saying good-bye to Gertrude Hall, the woman who had charted their course and was now departing with regrets of unfinished business. After proudly presenting the last diploma to the last graduate, she received a lengthy standing ovation, and took her seat on stage. Then she slumped forward. Someone drew the curtains. Dr. J. E. Moriarty and Miss Hall's personal physician, Dr. N. L. Brown, seated at her side on stage, were helpless to save her. Their revered director was declared dead on the spot from a cardiac arrest. One could not script a more befitting closing for the life of Gertrude M. Hall. Dr. E. P. Scarlett would describe it this way: "She died not in the comfortable haven of ease and indulgence, but in the full flood of action and high adventure, as nearly as possible the death she wished." Dr. Crosby Johnston paid further tribute: "We have lost a true and noble companion, a fellow worker whose life inspired us, a nurse whose like we will never forget, a teacher whose ideals will go unchallenged. Ave atque vale, friend of man."

Within one year of graduation, all members of the famous triumvirate that guided the Class of '59 through its training program

— Miss Hall, Miss Street and Miss Aikin — were gone. Miss Aikin took up a posting at the University of Western Ontario at the beginning of our senior year, stealing away when I was on vacation. But I never forgot her. Dorothy M. Dick (White '43) temporarily filled her position. Following the death of Miss Hall and the departure of Miss Street, two former CGH graduates took up the reins: Mrs. Edith Henry (Randall '30) became the new Director of Nursing, and Miss Eileen E. Jameson (Class of '45) assumed the position of Director of Nursing Education. They were assisted by Miss Muriel Sangster and Miss Jean Mackie respectively. These four dedicated women would devote their service to furthering Gertrude Hall's vision.

The Class of '74 was the last class to walk the stage. These sixty soldiers assuredly carried our banner with pride, in spite of all they were denied: one thousand additional hours of experience at the bedside that our forty-eight-hour-week provided; the adventure of an offsite hospital affiliation; a monthly $10.00 pay check (apparently they not only slaved without remuneration, they actually paid tuition); and the most notable attire in the school's entire history. The blue check gingham dress, topped with the flattering, waist-cinching bib and apron, had been discarded in favor of a shapeless pink dress. What, no bib? Where in the world did they stuff their cigarette packs, love letters, lipstick, Eatmore chocolate bars, or leftover sandwiches being hidden from Birdie Finch? Most regrettably, they were denied the life-altering reign of Gertrude M. Hall, Margaret M. Street, and R. Catherine Aikin.

The Calgary General Hospital School of Nursing graduated 2,960 nurses through a proud 79-year history. As it closed its doors behind the Class of 1974, clouds gathered overhead. At nightfall, they burst, and tears fell.

Chapter 4

— AFFILIATIONS —

A highlight of our training days was travelling to field hospitals. This aspect of our program provided a twofold benefit: a unique clinical experience not offered in our home hospital, and the personal challenge of adapting to an unfamiliar setting. Our school formed affiliations with four hospitals, including two within the city (the Alberta Crippled Children's Hospital and the Baker TB Sanatorium) and two out-of-town (the Provincial Mental Hospital in Ponoka and the Municipal Hospital in Taber). Our brief experience in public health — a few days visiting homes with the Victorian Order of Nurses or weighing babies with the City Health Department — have all but slipped from memory.

The Provincial Mental Hospital was the only affiliation of long standing, its association with the Calgary General and other training schools dating back to 1949 when it developed a psychiatric program for visiting students. (In 1939, the General had been the first hospital to provide the reverse arrangement, when it accepted students from the Ponoka four-year psychiatric program for their two-year clinical experience in general medicine.) On taking up their duties at the General, Gertrude Hall and Margaret Street quickly recognized the value of such an affiliation, and immediately sought to add further opportunities for their students. To this end, they formed liaisons with the sparkling new Children's Hospital, the ancient, run-down Baker San, and the welcoming, small town hospital in Taber. The Class of '56 pioneered the affiliations at the Children's and the San, while the Taber affiliation began a year later with the Class of '57.

We were allowed to declare our preferences, with the one exception that the degree program students were required by the

University of Alberta to attend the Baker San for their experience in Public Health. Miss Street, as always, rose to the monumental challenge of scheduling — a balancing act between granting our requests and fulfilling the staffing expectations of the affiliating hospitals. Her task was complicated, of course, if a student became ill or left the school entirely, and a posting opened that Miss Street was obligated to fill. Not infrequently, she was scrambling to find a replacement on short notice, and with Miss Hall's mandate that our education must be the first consideration, she would painstakingly scan her Master Plan for a suitable selection. I had the good fortune to receive three memorable assignments: the first, my personal choice of the Provincial Mental Hospital for psychiatry, and the other two — the Children's Hospital and the Baker San — as a replacement for unavailable classmates. The former coincided with my pediatric scheduling, and the latter was a late-in-the-day posting that fit with my tour of duty on general medicine.

The affiliations also came with an attractive bonus that in the eyes of many of us — at least in the eyes of those who were honest — held greater appeal than our clinical prospects, and that was the break we would get from the rules of our residence. Who could look me in the eye and deny the allure of being sprung from the confines of our own residence? Tigner jokes that travelling to Ponoka was like landing a *get out of jail free* card in Monopoly.

The Alberta Crippled Children's Hospital

The Alberta Crippled Children's Hospital began life as the Junior Red Cross Children's Hospital in 1922 in a three-story home on Eighteenth Avenue Southwest. The name Red Cross Crippled Children's Hospital was later adopted at a second location near Richmond Road. In 1952 the hospital set down roots in a sparkling new facility at 1820 Richmond Road, where it operated for over fifty years. When the Red Cross discontinued its sponsorship in 1957, the hospital adopted the name known to us. By 1960, under the mandate of the provincial government, it took the more encompassing name by which it's known today — Alberta Children's Hospital.

My first memory of Children's is of hauling my suitcase up the creaking steps of the big old house on Seventeenth Avenue South that would be my home for the next four weeks. It was a hot day in July, and my mind was travelling back in time to my childhood growing up in the neighborhood immediately north across the street. How well I remembered my curiosity over this very house — its tall, tall facade and its wide, wide glass veranda. Actually, I was beyond curious; I was bewitched. I longed to know who lived there, and since I never caught sight of anyone, I decided at a young age that the place was haunted. I could hardly believe I was now moving in with the ghosts.

My memory of the hospital itself is vague, except for its gleaming floors in bright, kid-friendly colors, that didn't announce "hospital." Many of the kids were long-term residents with orthopedic conditions such as post polio, scoliosis, Legg-Perthes, clubfeet — conditions we seldom encountered on pediatrics at the General. Zelenka has special memories of the life-changing surgeries performed during her stint, on babies with congenital harelip and cleft palate deformities. The miraculous results left a lasting impression on her.

For the many kids requiring lengthy stays, the hospital was their home — the place where they played, scrapped, attended school, and balked at eating their vegetables. We therefore had to assume mothering, disciplinarian roles in addition to our nursing duties. We faced an unfortunate state of affairs, however, in that our brief four-week tour meant we were perpetually the new kids on the block and the kids were the old-timers. Since the old-timers knew the routine far better than we did, they took delight in making life hell for us. McKenzie remembers actually feeling intimidated by the little devils, and Tomlinson confesses "it was the closest I ever came to quitting" when her first day was launched with a full-blown free-for-all as she attempted to ready her kids for morning school. The room became a battlefield of flying facecloths and socks, and the nurse-combatant's cap was repeatedly ripped from its moorings. I had the good fortune to be at Children's during Stampede Week, which brought welcome distractions. Children are much more cooperative when dressing for a chuckwagon breakfast rather than another morning in the classroom.

Stampede Week brought welcome distractions to Children's patients.

As classmates recall their student affiliations, I'm amused at how often it's the off-duty experiences that come to mind first. Jones, my roomie at Children's, has a much better memory of residence life there than I have, but then she wasn't preoccupied with ghosts.

She tells me I spent much of my off-duty time working on jigsaw puzzles. I have no recollection of this, but I trust Jones, and her memory of my preoccupation with something outside the study category is completely believable. Jones also remembers our housemother, Mrs. Blake, whose stern appearance belied the fact that she was actually a soft touch. Apparently Mrs. Softy was known to counsel students returning long past curfew, to "just sign 11:00 p.m." Jones! You didn't! I do remember Mrs. Blake maintaining a steady supply of bananas and peanut butter for our snacks — my favorite combo. One can work up quite an appetite doing jigsaw puzzles.

Falck recalls an evening when she was more of a scamp than the little monkeys she had cared for all day. She was posted to the more traditional, more restrictive residence than the house Jones and I lived in, and one night, before leaving on a date, she propped the fire escape door so she could return undetected after hours. She pulled off her scheme without a hitch. Thoroughly pleased with herself, she was more than eager to share the news of her successful exploit with fellow students the next morning over the breakfast table, but her date never learned how low he ranked on the interest scale; the main event of the night was testing her skills against the system. The satisfaction of the stunt is long remembered; the date, long forgotten. Jones and I aren't heartless enough to ask Falck what time she signed in.

Neufeld holds a fond memory of returning from a date to the *acceptable* entrance of that same residence. It was there that she received her first kiss from a special young man who was never forgotten. He wasted no time in proposing to the front door girl, and they lived happily ever after.

The Alberta Children's Hospital closed operations at its Richmond Road location on September 27, 2006, seamlessly transferring staff and patients to its new state-of-the-art facility opening on the University of Calgary's west campus. The old building — now called the Richmond Road Diagnostic and Treatment Centre — continues to provide health services to the community. It offers outpatient treatment services in Audiology, Eating Disorders, Child and Adolescent Mental Health, and Pre-school Speech. It also provides CT Scan and MRI diagnostic services.

The Baker Memorial Sanatorium

Directly across the river from Bowness Park sat the virtually self-contained community that formed the Baker Memorial Sanatorium, built in 1922. This institution had progressed through previous name changes, originating as the Central Alberta Sanatorium, then becoming the Keith Sanatorium and finally the Baker Sanatorium. Named after Dr. A. H. Baker, a long-serving superintendent, it was the only sanatorium in Canada specifically built for the ongoing care of tubercular war veterans. It provided 100 beds for veterans and 75 beds for civilians in a number of buildings spread along the banks of the Bow River. Since the river placed its residents in semi isolation, cut off from the city of Calgary, they almost became a "separate society," and that fact undoubtedly contributed to the long-standing stigma attached to the disease.

…maximum exposure to fresh air and sunshine.

I did not look forward to my four-week assignment at the San as an eleventh hour replacement. My grandfather had been stricken with TB as a young man, and although I never even knew him, I had long harbored an unnatural fear of the dreaded disease he had suffered. I could never erase the vision — learned from family tales — of Grandpa sleeping in a tent in the backyard in response to doctor's orders for "maximum exposure to fresh air and sunshine," or his forced career change to becoming a streetcar conductor for the same reason. The fact that he survived his infirmity and lived a reasonably long, healthy life, never gave me consolation.

Photo: courtesy Carolyn Kelly

First-day lectures on my arrival at the San only reinforced my inherent fear. Our instructor repeatedly stressed the extreme infectiousness of the tubercle bacillus as she demonstrated the meticulous technique we must employ to protect ourselves. By the end of the day, I was convinced that warding off the billions of breeding bacilli afloat in the air was going to be futile, regardless of my best technique practices. I had to be inhaling a freshly hatched batch with every breath, even through a mask. My only comfort was the sun, which I believed to be my best ally as I thought back on Grandpa camping out in the backyard. Half a century later, his treatment was being endorsed right here by the San, with its routine of filing its little band of children outside for a daily sunning.

Everything seemed old to me at the San — staff, who had been there forever; the flaking buildings; and the morning staple — a sorry plate of bone dry bread in the centre of our breakfast table. I have no memory of the kippers and cod liver oil pills that Hill laughingly points out accompanied the bread. How could I forget? Breakfast at the San gave me a whole new appreciation for the above-average fare we were served at our home cafeteria. The dreary, tomblike residence made me long for my buddies on North Eight back home, and the hospital's split shift schedule effectively killed any chance for a social life. So I used the breaks between shifts to walk through Bowness Park for my daily sun treatment. A tennis court bade from a corner of the property, but remained barren as I unsuccessfully sought a contender.

The San's tight budget was evident, and went well beyond the dry bread. Matthews remembers the staff reusing packing containers to sterilize dressings and surgical instruments. And she shakes her head in disbelief as she recalls the inconceivable practice of transforming the low-grade tri-fold toilet paper, commonly found in public washrooms at the time, into masks, a high volume item.

Towels wore thin and bedding was mended and patched until it disintegrated. The only disposable articles were the toilet paper masks. Everything else was restored and reused.

I reported for duty with a great deal of unease, battling my fears as I entered this unfamiliar, contagious setting. I was assigned a large room of men, all long-term on strict bed rest, which meant an around-the-clock repetitive regimen of meal trays, nap times, medications, bed baths and bedpans — day in and day out, month after month. I could not fathom how they endured this depressing, monotonous routine throughout an extended separation from their families, with such patience and grace. Before I knew it, they were caring for me, drawing me from my selfish, inward thoughts, and banishing my fears. I now look back on the Baker San with warm fondness of friendships won. I only hope I was worthy of my patients' charity.

The San operated at overflow capacity up until the Aberhart Memorial Sanatorium opened in Edmonton in 1951, relieving some of the caseload. As well, by this time, the use of antimicrobial drugs was beginning to shorten confinement periods, a circumstance that eventually led to treatment of victims on an outpatient basis. Within a year of my affiliation at the Baker San, empty beds were becoming the new norm, and the facility began converting newly available space for the treatment of the mentally challenged, many relocating from the Michener Centre in Red Deer. By the summer of 1979, the San's only remaining TB service was its outpatient clinic, which was then transferred to the Foothills Hospital. The old Baker San was now known as the Baker Centre for the Services of the Handicapped. In 1987, these residents were further transferred to alternate accommodations, and the Centre's peeling doors groaned shut for the last time. Its weary, abandoned buildings disappeared from the site two years later. Its magnificent grounds, featuring a grand alley of trees that lined the original lone access road to the hospital, remained behind to form the backdrop of our beautiful Baker Park. The trees are the one lasting vestige of the Sanatorium's memorable history.

The Taber Municipal Hospital

Gertrude Hall knew the benefit of experience in a small hospital from her own early background, and so she set out to provide the opportunity for her students. Her resulting alliance with the Taber Municipal Hospital was unique, and the six-week program involved CGH students only. Those who experienced Taber all sing praises of the special treatment they received as the only students in the facility. They loved the way the graduate nurses treated them as equals.

Two affiliates at a time travelled to Taber, a town of 3,500 people in southern Alberta — friendly, hardworking folk happily going about their business and contributing to their community. Until my buddy Zelenka took me home to Taber one weekend to visit her family on their wheat farm, the town only meant sugar beets to me. Molyneux's period there as a student, however, gave rise to a whole new association for her — dust — dust like she'd never imagined possible. Her memory of the hospital has faded with the years, but the three-day dust storm she endured remains crystal clear.

Hospital staff took their meals in a cafeteria across the road, and during times when the dust storm was in full fury, they could barely navigate their way to lunch. Molyneux cringes when describing the unpleasant sensation of munching through an entire meal with gritty teeth. And she couldn't believe how the grit found its way into every nook and cranny of the hospital, ostensibly even making its way through the closed doors of unused rooms. It was brought home to her when she entered a closed room and lifted the spread from the foot of a bed, to discover the distinct strip of white it left behind.

Taber Municipal Hospital

The Taber Municipal Hospital had about 70 beds. Its lower level housed medical wards and pediatrics; the upper level, obstetrics, a nursery and surgery, including two surgical theatres at the end of the hall. The occasional autopsy was performed in the basement morgue by one of the physicians, who was faithfully assisted by a retired navy medic. Collver and Groeneveld, who travelled to Taber

Photo: courtesy Cathy Heisen

together, remember the day they were confronted with such an occurrence.

They turned up for duty one morning just as one of the physicians on the floor announced he was on his way to perform an autopsy. "Would you like to come along and view the procedure?" he offered, eager, as always, to contribute to the student nurses' learning experience. The girls knew they had the option of attending or not, but life as they knew it under the domination of doctors ruled out refusal as an option in their minds, even for an impromptu proposal such as this. So they agreed to attend, though with much trepidation.

They arrived at the cold, damp morgue utterly unprepared for the disturbing procedure they were about to witness. Goose bumps danced on their arms, and rapid gasps for breath quickly brought on a queasiness. The doctor arrived in his water-repellent scrubs, greeted the girls cordially, and set about preparing his equipment for the job. Then the assistant rolled in the deceased, and they made the shocking discovery that it was a wee blonde-haired cherub, no more than five years old. Memories of the recent loss of her own precious sister flooded Collver's mind, and a cold clamminess spread over her body. Grappling for air above a thundering heartbeat, she turned to her friend, and gasped, "I cannot stay for this." An understanding Groeneveld willingly accompanied her out the door, and remained at her side until she had recovered from the unsettling experience.

The story brings to mind how often we sisters administered to one another through occasions such as this in the course of our training days. I'm also reminded that this story would not have taken place at our home hospital. Gertrude Hall, in spite of a goal to toughen us as necessary for the job, drew the line at us assisting or witnessing an autopsy. She saw no redeeming value in exposing us to this procedure, and to our gratitude, personally protected us from it.

The difference between the casual operating style of this small town hospital and the rigid rules of our big city hospital was quickly evident. For Peterson, it began with an early encounter with the assistant matron. She remembers arriving at work suffering an agonizing case of menstrual cramps, and the matron spontaneously issuing a treatment plan as if Peterson was a bona fide patient. "Sign out two 292s every four hours as needed," she ordered casually, "and just list yourself as Dr. Hormone's patient." Any such illicit activity with controlled medication at the Calgary General could have been career-ending. But the lowly student does not question authority, and so Peterson dutifully dosed herself with pain relief as ordered, finished her day's duties, and went home to bed with a hot water bottle. Later that night, the concerned matron appeared at her door to check on her charge, whom she found resting comfortably... very comfortably. Slowly the reason for this surprise house call registered on Peterson's foggy brain — a smile crept onto her face as she remembered the matron administering a double shot of brandy with her last 292 of the day.

Peterson has two other memories of Taber that have surfaced through the years. The first was a young lad who turned up with an extensive burn to his torso. His horrified mother was even more horrified at the thought of rushing her son to hospital in a soiled shirt, so she insisted he make a change. Of course, removing the soiled shirt took the first swath of skin with it, and then Peterson was confronted with attempting to minimize further damage by soaking and cutting off the clean shirt. Her order to her patient that day was, "If you have the misfortune to burn yourself like this again, don't come back in a clean shirt." *So much for my mother's edict, "Always wear clean underwear because you never know when... "*

Peterson's second memory centres around diapering instructions she received in the nursery. She was working with cloth diapers, of course. She was taught to give them a twist in the middle, which produced a more absorbent diaper, yet less bulk between baby's legs. She also learned to make an extra fold in the front for boys and in the back for girls. Countless times through the years, when diapering her own five children "Taber-style," she looked back with gratitude for these invaluable tips learned in the Taber nursery.

The hospital closed in the late eighties, and was demolished piece by piece to make way for a government building that was erected on its property three years later. A new municipal hospital was built approximately one mile west of the original site.

The Provincial Mental Hospital – Ponoka

I travelled by train with three of my buddies — Blewett, Dingwall and Lovewell — to the central Alberta town of Ponoka for our eight-week clinical experience in psychiatry at the Provincial Mental Hospital (PMH). I cringe at the thought of the hospital's official designation when it opened in 1911 — the Provincial Mental Hospital for the Insane. Girls from seven nursing schools throughout the province rolled into the station that day to make up a combined class of eighteen affiliates. It was the summer of '58, and we were on the cusp of becoming sophisticated seniors, ready to take on the world. What an exciting place to start!

I wasn't prepared for the size and beauty of the institution, its large circle of buildings spreading over a magnificent piece of land a mile or so south of the town. Its beautifully tended grounds gave it the look of an idyllic little town one might see painted on a postcard. It was a nearly self-sustaining community with its own farm operations providing much of its food, and supervised patients making up a huge portion of the labor force. I have not forgotten the hardworking women assigned to waiting tables in the cafeteria.

They performed with such diligence I had to learn to eat with one hand anchoring my plate to the table, or they'd sweep it away if I paused to chew. A number of the medical staff worked and lived on the property, giving the institution an air of operating in its own little world.

From my second floor room, my eyes light up when I spot a tennis court from my window. I dig out my racquet, and everything else can wait. "C'mon Dingwall," I announce, "we're going for a game."

"Ha," she says, and cracks up. "You've gotta be joking. Have you ever seen me play tennis?" But I wasn't joking — I refused to spend another affiliation staring at an empty tennis court.

"We won't keep score," I persist, "and you can ignore the lines. All you have to do is hit the ball over the net."

"Okay, but remember, this is your idea," she warns, adding a barely audible muttering, something like, "You'll live to regret this." By the time we reach the court, all thoughts of the nursing experience we are here for have been pushed aside by the tennis challenge before us. I begin with a nice easy ball to her racquet, and she nails it on the sweet spot.

"That's a beaut, Dingwall," I cheer, as the ball floats fifteen feet above my head, "except I said over the *net,* not over the fence." I retrieve the ball, serve again, and watch it sail from sight a second time. Quickly, I become painfully aware that we have locked in a serve, over-the-fence, go-fetch routine that defies altering. Begrudgingly, I accept it as a signal that the time has come to address serious matters — time to unpack our uniforms and prepare for the *inside* world of PMH.

I arrived at PMH with the romantic notion that the world of mental illness was emerging from its grim, archaic history; that

The Provincial Mental Hospital – Ponoka

the relatively recent advent of psychotropic drugs was producing miracles; that the sick and abandoned were being made whole again; that the stigma of mental disease was at last breaking down. It was the dawn of hope, and I was about to be part of it. I was going to make a difference. Then I unlocked the door to Female Five.

I entered a horrifying scene: ragged-looking women either pacing the floor compulsively or huddling in a medicated stupor in a spot they had staked as theirs. Those too violent for the staff to manage were caged — pathetic souls crouching on floor mattresses behind bars, marking time by rocking back and forth, back and forth... day after day, year after year. Their state of affairs prior to the the use of *Equanil* and *Largactil* — medications that offered some relief to a patient's agitation — was beyond imagining.

Medical histories revealed heartrending stories of patients who, twenty years prior, had been delivered to the hospital's care by a family member, who, perceiving the stigma of their loved one's illness, never returned. Abandonment drove these victims into the depths of some obscure world that claimed them forever. They had no one, and they owned nothing. My hat was off to the staff, mostly kind and caring, who patiently persevered to find solutions for these long-suffering charges committed to their care. Yet it seemed to me that their earnestly discussed treatment plans either failed or were lost in translation on the wards. I perceived life there to be a futile, repetitive cycle of custodial care, each day unfolding just as the day before had, and the day before that.

I especially remember the woman who incessantly wrote letters of solicitation — thousands of them — slipping them to us students on the sly, trusting we'd recognize how she had been wronged, and set the wheels in motion to spring her from captivity. Class after class of affiliates left PMH with one or more of her letters written in her oversized, swirling script with her unmistakable i's dotted with little circles. One of my letters began, "Dear Miss King, Lord Bramwell, noted British Jurist, declares that the MacNaghton Rules are the basis for determining sanity..."

I weep at the thought of this sad, tormented woman hunched over a table in the corner of the common room, scratching furiously on scraps of paper retrieved from waste baskets in an everlasting crusade for her cause.

The indignity of bath day will forever haunt me — the groups of agitated women huddled in various states of undress awaiting their turn for one of the yawning bathtubs lining the large, damp common bathroom. I can still feel my blue check dress sticking to my back and my starched white apron beginning to wilt as the morning progressed. I can see the women whose habit it was to bind their small treasures in scraps of cotton and pin them to their undershirts for safekeeping. They would arrive for their baths with these comical little pouches bobbing on their chests, and before disrobing, each pouch had to be removed and painstakingly re-pinned to a clean undershirt. It was a task they were unwilling to trust with me. And so, I would watch and wait as each one unpinned and re-pinned on her own, stepping into the tub only when they were assured their prized possessions were securely in place. What was it they bound in those little scraps of cloth, I wondered, some so fiercely taut they were hard as rocks? Maybe it *was* rocks. Or was it odds and ends scavenged from the ward on their daily patrol — a hair clip, a button, a penny? I held out hope that at least some contained a significant article, maybe a piece of jewellery from bygone days — a keepsake that could transport them back to happier times.

Meanwhile, Dingwall, my over-the-top tennis buddy, took her *inside* PMH experience to a whole new level as she engaged admission procedures for an elderly woman. Having ushered her tiny, birdlike charge into one of the small rooms reserved for the process, she was at last winding up the paperwork, when suddenly, without warning, the little bird took flight, slamming the door behind her and locking in her protector. Dingwall, a tall, strapping, *unbirdlike* girl, was left with egg on her face, as she peered through the slot in the door at Miss Warbler skittering off to freedom. A feeble, embarrassed cry for help was eventually heard by an unbelieving admissions clerk.

In the end, PMH had a marked impact on all of us who affiliated there, opening our eyes to a world of lost souls isolated from society — gritty survivors in a field of medicine that, in our eyes, was failing them. Some of my classmates were downright traumatized by their Ponoka experience, suffering what would be labelled today as post traumatic stress disorder on returning home. At the very least, we all suffered the disappointment of failing to achieve dreams we had harbored — illusions really, that we were going to make a difference. My hope is that all my sisters experienced at least some moments, as I did, when the sun came out and pushed back the dark.

I came of age in Ponoka — on two fronts: firstly, by attaining the exalted status of a senior student, and then a few short weeks later, by reaching the age of twenty-one. I was now an official adult. Blewett, Dingwall, Lovewell and I were fully aware of our new senior standing the day we flipped our calendars to September, although we longed to affirm the milepost with our sisters rejoicing together back home. Then one day after class, our house mother greeted us with a large envelope postmarked Calgary, and our spirits lifted. We tore it open, and out tumbled four familiar navy bands with a congratulatory letter from R. Catherine Aikin. It was official — we were seniors! We had thought this day would never come. We knew the senior bands symbolized mature responsibility; we sat cross-legged on our beds, and pinned them on our caps like giddy school girls who'd just won ribbons at a grade six track meet.

My twenty-first birthday is one I will never forget. I was separated from my entire family by hundreds of miles, so I was mentally prepared for a day like any other. It was a Monday, and I was scheduled to work the 1:00 p.m. - 9:00 p.m. shift. The moment I arrived on duty, something told me it was not a day like any other on the ward. The women were abuzz with excitement, although I was given no clue as to why. With unusual restlessness they criss-crossed the common room aimlessly, stopping only now and then to whisper and giggle in groups. Eventually, the charge nurse gathered together a select group, and informed me of her plan to accompany them to occupational therapy for a couple of hours in an effort to restore calm. The plan worked. It was about 3:15 p.m. when my peaceful interlude with those left behind in my care came to an abrupt end.

I heard the key unlock the door, and looked up to see the charge nurse leading her flock — like Mother Goose leading her goslings — back home. Now, however, the flock was more animated than ever as it shuffled along in a tightly knit cluster directly toward me, coming to a stop at my feet. Then it parted like the Red Sea, and out stepped a tall, thin woman, almost overcome with emotion at her honored appointment as bearer of the afternoon's project — a magnificent birthday cake, tenderly decorated with frosting and sprinkles, and crowned with 21 candles. It was beyond imagining how this fidgety, hyperactive band of women achieved this culinary feat, but I know I've never had a more beautiful birthday cake.

A table appeared from somewhere, and the cake was carefully placed on it. Then the proud, happy bakers encircled the birthday girl, and as the candles were lit, they broke into song: "Happy Birthday to you..." Slowly, others in the room — even some who had seemingly disconnected from the world years prior — timidly trickled toward the celebration, hesitantly at first, then adding full voice to the singing of "Many long years to you..." As I blinked back the tears, my eyes circled the room taking in each face of this precious ragtag ring of women offering me their hearts on my special day, finally coming to rest on the face of our charge nurse who had simply given in to her emotions. Although I knew her to be a kind-hearted soul, it surprised me to see tears running down the cheeks of this seasoned veteran. As we worked together cutting and serving the cake, I learned the reason for her momentary loss of composure. "Did you see Josephine?" she whispered breathlessly. "I've never heard her utter a sound in all my years serving this ward, and today she sang Happy Birthday to *you!*" I knew at that moment that this would be the birthday of a lifetime.

Lastly, there was another element to PMH that travelled home on the tongues of every affiliate: its notorious — if not scandalous — single male society. The local boys lived an enviable dream of eyeing eighteen new, fresh-faced females circulating through their town every two months. I have since learned a cheeky lot even maintained a log of their arrival schedules, and would hang out at the train station to size up the merchandise stepping onto the platform. A handful of those had further audacity to rate the *fillies* with stars, as one would rate a movie or a restaurant or a motel. My guess is that if you flashed them a smile you automatically got three stars, while accepting an invitation for coffee and conversation at Bud's Cafe landed you four.

Bud's Café placemat

Bud's placemat: courtesy Joy Whitehouse

My personal experience with the local boys began the first week, when my roommate, Lovewell, greeted me at the top of the stairs one night on my return to residence from evening duty.

"I've got us a date for Friday night," she enthuses. I know in an instant that her four-star blonde hair had caught the eye of some guy.

"What do you mean, you've got *us* a date?" I shoot back. "I'm perfectly capable of getting my own date, and I don't happen to be looking right now." I stomp off to our room, and that's the end of it... at least in my mind. But not in Lovewell's mind as she follows me into the room.

"You will come though, won't you?" she asks uneasily.

"No, I have no intention of coming. I have never been on a blind date in my life and I am not about to start now. How in the world did you cook this up behind my back anyway?"

"Well, this guy named Greg called and asked me out, and I didn't want to go on a date with a stranger by myself, so I said I would go if he got a date for my roommate."

"And of course, you didn't see fit to consult the roommate," I huff. "Well forget it, I'm not going. Call this Greg person and tell him that."

"I can't."

"Why not?"

"I don't know his phone number."

"Well, Ponoka's a pretty small town, you'll be able to find it in the phonebook."

"No I won't."

"How do you know before you've even tried?"

"I don't know his last name." She's grinning sheepishly now, but I'm not about to bail her out of this impossible situation she has gotten herself into.

"Well then, have a good time with the two of them," I announce firmly, "because I am still not going." Now she's on her knees.

"You have to come this once," she begs. "I promise I'll never do this to you again." I can see I'm in for pleading and pestering until Friday, and it's only Wednesday. So I give in.

Friday night came, and so did Greg (with no last name) and his benevolent friend who had the unfortunate assignment of taking a sour, angry roommate on the town, all in the name of friendship. Needless to say, the meeting of these two recruited chaperones was not a story that began, "There eyes met across a crowded room... " But incredibly, it *was* the beginning of a story — one that unfolded into a love story. And it continues...

Recruited chaperones begin a life journey.

In the late sixties, PMH began turning over its chronic cases to the care of communities in Red Deer and Calgary as well as its own town of Ponoka. Unfortunately, the community psychiatric nursing programs designed to monitor and support these former patients all too often failed them. The hospital is now known as The Centennial Centre for Mental Health and Brain Injury. It is a state-of-the-art facility that maintains its time-honored history of providing comprehensive mental health services in addition to providing world-renowned treatment for the brain injured.

Chapter 5

– DUTY BOUND –

Breaking In

After we had spent ten weeks tormenting Mrs. Chase and Mrs. Sanborn in the practice room under the watchful eye of our instructors, they turned us loose. Were they breathing confidence that they'd prepared us for the task, or were they gulping with misgivings that, in fact, they were tossing us to the wolves? I remember walking through the tunnel that first day with emotions flip-flopping between excitement and fear. I was about to prove my worth as a real live nurse — the genuine article — but that meant facing the terrifying prospect of caring for real live patients. I would no longer have the inert Mrs. Chase to accommodate all my clumsy blunders with eternal patience and grace; a living Mrs. Chase might conceivably have little tolerance for my incompetence. The more I thought about this undertaking, the more it seemed way beyond my reach.

We dispersed throughout the hospital in groups for our first assignments, and I suspect that each one of us can still name our first ward these fifty years later. I began on West Six, a general medicine ward that seemed to have a large geriatric population. Of course, when you're eighteen, anyone over forty-five is geriatric. My first assignment was water jugs — to deliver fresh ice water to everyone's bedside. It seemed that the entire Calgary General water brigade was made up of my sisters and me that day. After all, that was the most rudimentary task the people in charge could drum up for us — one that any probationer could handle. Except there was a fly in the ointment. We were dressed in full uniform, which masked our first-day status to the patients. Every delivery of a water jug therefore risked an encounter we weren't equipped to handle: "Nurse, can you change my draw sheet. I don't know how it got all wet." We quickly learned to deliver the water jug — and retreat — at breakneck speed to thwart any such a confrontation.

The second complication for me personally was my assigned partner, D. Miller, a hall mate from residence. Now, I'm smug enough to suggest that individually we were reasonably intelligent girls, and unquestionably responsible, but when teamed together we became a pair of harebrained, giggling fools. Perhaps seeing the funny side of everything was our method of coping. In any event, I can still see us snickering our way down the south wing of West Six, ice cubes skidding around the top of our rattling water jug cart. The first room on our left — a semiprivate — was home to a notoriously cantankerous old woman with a reputation for automatically making some outrageous demand as you passed her bed, or tearing a strip off you for something you knew nothing about. As we reached her door, I looked across the cart at Miller.

"You do this room," I say, nonchalantly. "I'll get the next one."

"I'm not going in there again," comes Miller's quick reply. "That old lady by the window reamed me out the last time I was in there, and I still don't know what her problem was."

"Well, here's your big chance to find out," I joke, waving her toward the door. "Chances are pretty good she'll hit you with it again."

"No thanks," she says, shaking her head. "You go find out what her problem is."

Finally, my black humor rises to the occasion, and I announce, "Okay, I'll do Mrs. Crab's water jug, and I'll just give her a piece of my mind while I'm at it." Then with head erect and shoulders back, I sail into the room with the cockiness of a Yorkshire Terrier that's just won best in show. Of course, once inside, my posturing evaporates, and I gingerly inch my way across the room.

Mrs. Crab is sitting upright in her bed, and seems almost in a trance as she gazes out the window. I am silently hoping she really is in a trance, so that I can deposit this water jug and sneak away undetected. I tiptoe to her bedside table, ease the jug into place, and am about to make my escape when she lets loose. No, not with her usual barrage of demands or complaints; she's perched on a bedpan... and she's clearly been stowing more gas than *Trans Canada Gas* stores in a year. I stagger from the room to find Miller outside the door, doubled over the utility cart in a fit of hysterics. "Yup, you sure told her," she gags, barely able to lift her head. I collapse on top of her. We eventually complete our task, but we don't regain our composure for the rest of the day.

Jones was one of the lucky ones — no cranky geriatrics on her first assigned ward — she was sent to orthopedics where, at first glance, her entire patient roster appeared to be young, healthy jocks unrestrained by broken bones. "Boy," she beamed to herself as she waltzed from room to room slinging water jugs, "this nursing is going to be even better than I figured." Jones was eventually sent to West Six.

Attending to flowers was an early assignment along with water jugs, and with delivery came the added responsibility of keeping the flowers alive. Gift flowers seldom came in the arranged bouquets of today. Visitors would come with cut flowers, either from the florist or their own gardens, and we would arrange them in a vase and label them. But the real task took place at the end of the day when all flowers had to be removed from every room, then returned again the following morning. The thinking was that flowers and plants used up the precious oxygen in the air.

On some wards, every night we placed the flowers in a row on the floor outside each room, while other wards preferred to pile them on a gurney and put them to bed in a service room. It took considerable time and fussing to get plants and flowers arranged, watered, bedded, and delivered to their rightful owners.

Tomlinson remembers delivering top-heavy gladioli in a vase that was too small. It toppled off the over-the-bed table into the lap of a surprised patient, giving him a dousing and complicating her first two assignments of the day — flower delivery and the morning bed bath. She took some consolation in the knowledge that her mishap was not an isolated incident during gladiola season. We never addressed the possibility that caring for flowers was not advancing our nursing skills. We did as we were told.

Death Visits

For three of my sisters, there was no humor in their early water jug experiences. They relate comparable stories that go something like this: "I pushed open the door and found a little old lady propped up in bed. I said good morning to her, and explained why I was there. She didn't answer. As I came closer to put the water jug on her bedside table, I noticed she was very still... and then I realized she wasn't breathing. For a minute I just stared at her." We all remember that first encounter with death.

For some of us, death came unannounced through a chance encounter such as delivering a meal tray or a water jug. For others, it came in a more intimate setting as we were actively engaged in a patient's care. For all of us unworldly eighteen-year-olds, it was a shocking circumstance for which we were entirely unprepared. Our responses to death were as varied as our personalities.

My patient was a thickset, rugged-looking man in his late seventies, with the whitest hair I'd ever seen. It was my first unsupervised bed bath, and although my patient was mostly unresponsive, I was not grasping the gravity of his situation. I performed every step of the bath to the letter, and stood back to admire the pleasing results of a stranger at peace, in a bed I had meticulously draped in crisp white cotton. Then suddenly his respirations became irregular. I instinctively put my hand on his arm and spoke his name. He did not respond. Within seconds, he took his last breath. I remained still with my hand on his arm. I was shocked and unsettled by my patient's rapid departure, yet my initial reaction was to dignify his death with a moment of quiet. Then I fled the room.

E. Smith relates a similar story of her patient expiring while she was attentively washing his feet. The shock of this surprising first encounter with death remains vivid for her to this day — so, too, has the kindness of the graduate nurses who attended to both her and the deceased with calm and caring. Some of my sisters tell of wanting to run and hide that first time, fearing they'd be blamed for the death. Yet most join E. Smith in voicing admiration for the experienced nurses who eased the situation for them with compassionate professionalism. Finch especially remembers the RN on pediatrics who had the forethought to hustle the attending student nurse out of the nursery to avoid the possibility of her witnessing an infant's death. A babe cradled in the RN's arms had just arrived for admission; he took his last breath as she placed him in a crib. We never got toughened to the loss of a child.

How could I forget my first experience with the death of a tiny soul who lost her chance for life before it began? It was on Emergency, and a young, heartbroken mother was struggling emotionally and physically with a pregnancy that had failed late in the game, dashing her dream for this longed-for child. Together we awaited its passing, an unearthly circumstance which I felt hopelessly unprepared to handle. *How can I make this easier for this woman?* I agonized. *How long will this take? What will the fetus look like?* Then as I set about performing the shave prep ordered by her obstetrician, my heart stopped; five tiny toes were working their way into the outer world. I decided it was okay to shed a tear with the weeping mom. Actually, I had no say.

One of my classmates relates a tale of her patient dying in the bathtub, a state-of-affairs that sent her into a panic. As Mrs. Dove slipped below the surface of the water, our frantic sister instinctively reached in to pull her up, but time and again, kept losing her grip because of the slipperiness of her patient. A fellow classmate appeared on the scene to discover her near-hysterical, thoroughly drenched sister wrestling with this impossible situation, and called for help. One week later, those attending lectures in nursing arts, received a special directive from the instructor — one not included in the course's textbook: "The first thing to do if a patient faints or expires in the bathtub is to <u>pull the plug</u>." A few class members were heard to murmur, "How stupid does she think we are?"

Vital Signs

The first encounter with death was understandably unnerving, but in fact, everything we faced for the first time loomed large in our eyes, whether it was the correct protocol for greeting a superior or the mundane task of caring for flowers. Neufeld remembers her first day on obstetrics, awaiting instructions in the chart room. Protocol issues were the last thing on her mind when the supervisor, Miss Matheson arrived. Neufeld failed to stand immediately, and that faux pas did not meet the expectations or approval of her disgruntled supervisor. "You are to rise when a supervisor, or anyone of importance comes in," Miss Matheson announced curtly. Embarrassed and apologetic, Neufeld clambered awkwardly to her feet. Following the incident, a bewildering question weighed on

Neufeld's mind: *How am I to know who's important?*

Eventually, however, we got down to the serious stuff of taking vital signs — TPRs (temperature, pulse and respiration) and blood pressures. Temperatures were taken the proper way, not with an automatic probe gadget stuck in the ear, but with a real glass mercury thermometer under the tongue. The TPR trays contained two glass jars, one carrying the clean thermometers, and another for the used, which were then shipped off to the Central Supply Room for cleaning.

Taking temperatures seemed a simple enough task, but a number of things could — and did — go wrong. Shaking down the mercury with a flick of the wrist opened the door for the occasional flying thermometer, and apparently on one occasion, a whole tray of them flew when a classmate collided with a physician making rounds. A further risk was that a patient would bite and break the thermometer, a situation we avoided at all cost by selecting a different orifice for those we deemed at peril. Lastly, we had the odd smart aleck patient — often a long-term resident — who dreamed up a trick or two to throw us off stride. I remember one young paraplegic who slipped his thermometer out of his mouth and rubbed it furiously on the sheets while I circled the room attending to his roommates. He exploded with laughter at my alarm over his high-grade fever.

Respirations were pretty simple to count as long as the patient was breathing, and once we got the hang of finding a pulse, that too, became second nature. Except for Fraser... who had trouble when background radios complicated the job for her. Apparently she had a strong tendency to count the beat of the music instead of the beat of the heart. "Let's face it," she admits, "I've always had a terrible time staying on task." I shudder to think of the pulses she recorded when *Rock Around the Clock* was playing.

There was a trick to taking blood pressures accurately, and practising on one another no doubt produced a few cases of hypertension. I remember our clinical instructors double-checking our readings for accuracy a number of times before trusting us to perform this important task on our own. Finch could have used a back-up the day she was pumping up the cuff on a patient, and the squeeze ball popped off the sphygnomometer and rolled under the bed, where it came to rest in the far reaches. What could she do except crawl under on her hands and knees to retrieve it? She was just backing out, when the head nurse arrived on rounds with one of the attending physicians. Eyes rolling at the sight of Finch's emerging bottom, the doctor turned to the head nurse and asked, "Is this how you treat all your students?"

Doctor's Orders

Unfortunately, we typically remember the doctors who were short on humor the best — those with a superior, even almighty attitude that put us in the subservient role where they reckoned we belonged. At least Neufeld didn't have to ponder whether they were important. She stood smartly, as we all did, whenever a doctor approached the desk or entered a classroom.

Two doctors who infamously terrorized us, especially in the operating room, were Dr. H. E. Gibson and Dr. St. Clair Robertson. Both men were known to throw instruments or extracted body parts across the room at the least provocation. Were we really that inept as assistants, or was all that juvenile instrument-flinging an insecure bid for dominance? Or were they just plain angry? At what?

I remember being posted to the OR still in my junior year, way before I felt ready to undertake such an assignment. I didn't have Finch's luck when scrubbing for the first time. Her surgeon, perceiving her terror, prescribed the perfect antidote. "Just pretend everyone in the room is buck naked," he grinned. She stifled giggles throughout the entire operation as she imagined her pot-bellied mentor in the altogether.

There was no giggling on my first day. I was assigned an appendectomy with the dreaded Dr. Robertson, who began with his usual impatience toward his assistants — novice, nervous me as his scrub nurse alongside a calm, confident pro circulating. Both she and Dr. Robertson were British, which meant they shared a lingo that was occasionally foreign to me, but I knew everything was under control in the hands of this capable woman. We got underway with surprising ease, and I was even beginning to question all the negative press I'd heard about the doctor, when suddenly the wheels fell off. With alarming speed, Dr. Flinger was revealing the reputation he had earned, his true colors rising rapidly to the surface until I found myself face to face with an out-of-control madman, raging incoherently about something I wondered if even he understood. I was dumbfounded, then more so when the circulating nurse flashed a quick response. "Dr. Robertson, I'll remind you to treat my student with dignity," she said slowly and deliberately, her eyes glaring directly at his over their masks. I couldn't believe the fearlessness of this woman standing up against Asclepius himself. Dr. Robertson momentarily proceeded in stunned silence, but it did not last. I must have handed him the wrong sized forceps for suturing — or committed some similarly life-threatening error — because the next thing I knew, he had erupted into a full-blown rant, and the forceps were sailing across the room.

"Miss King," I hear the circulating nurse order above his tirade, "you may be excused. You do not need to take this."

"Oh, I'm all right," I say unconvincingly. "I will stay until until Dr. Robertson closes." At this point I'm not feeling great loyalty to the surgeon, but I do feel an obligation to the patient to see this to the end. However, Nurse Braveheart has other plans.

"Miss King, I am *ordering* you to leave," she says. I waver; *who am I answerable to anyway?* But I don't mull it over for long, because I look up to see Chief Braveheart stepping into my sterile field where she intentionally contaminates me with her unsterile hands, forcing my exit. I am speechless. I back away in silence, leaving an also speechless Dr. Robertson to sew up his patient unassisted. I know I can trust his circulating nurse to oversee the patient's survival.

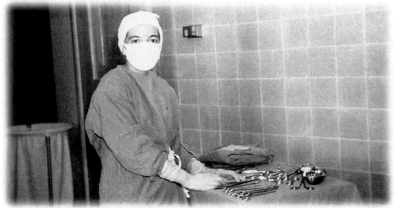

Scrubbed and waiting...

Tomlinson arrived at the OR when she was a little further down the road than I. That gave her no advantage technically, but it did afford her the confidence of greater maturity. Mind you, maturity wasn't enough to get her through her first operation, a tonsillectomy. The stuffy operating room was crowded with six classmates surrounding the table as observers, Tomlinson balancing on a stool to see over their heads. Undisturbed by the sight of blood, she was taking everything comfortably in stride... until the surgeon began suctioning. That did it — she instantly began teetering with queasiness. The attending clinical instructor was quick to spot trouble. "Miss Tomlinson, are you okay?" she whispers in concern. It was the last thing Tomlinson remembers before waking up on a stretcher in the recovery room.

Tomlinson was not the first or last to faint on the job, and the triggers were as different as we were. A number of classmates describe procedures in the mouth or nose as their biggest challenges, while others rank vein stripping at the top of their squeamish scale. Still others remember reeling the first time they witnessed the miracle of childbirth. Eventually, time toughened most of us. But there were an unfortunate few who turned green around the gills at almost every eventuality — even the sight of blood — and they had to face up to the reality that nursing was not for them. We bade them a sad farewell.

One particular tonsillectomy during my posting in the OR did not allow anyone the time to pass out. The patient was a curly-haired five-year-old, and as the anesthetic was being administered, her heart stopped. The surgeon and the anesthetist desperately pulled out everything in their black bags to bring the child back, but her little body lay blue and lifeless. An alert circulating nurse, aware that a cardiac surgeon was scrubbing up across the way, ran for his help, and apprised him of all methods already undertaken to save the child as she led him back to the scene. By the time they arrived, he had determined the only solution. He calmly reached for a scalpel, and with a decisive swipe of the blade, opened the child's chest and began massaging her heart. We gasped at this startling action, unimaginable for the time. The deathly silent room erupted into cheers of joy when the little heart quivered, then began pulsing rhythmically.

I hiked up to pediatrics the next day to assure myself that this child was truly still with us. I found a rosy-cheeked little lamb bubbling to show me her surprise. Raising her nightshirt, she pointed to the scar on her chest, and said, beaming, "Look nurse, they took out my tonsils." I wonder when her parents told her the truth. I expect she still has her tonsils.

It was a new Tomlinson who arrived in the night to scrub for Dr. St. Clair Robertson, whose patient's life lay in the balance due to a perforated ulcer. Even though jolted from sleep in the residence call room (how we hated nights there, tossing fitfully for hours with one eye on the clock and the other on the phone), she resolved to stay on her feet this time, and that much she did. Still, she was understandably nervous.

Dealing with Dr. Robertson's bad temper is one thing, but deciphering his British terminology and unusual methods is another. (How are we to know that "fingers" mean forceps? "Miss Clumsy, have you got some long fingers there?" "I don't think my fingers are any longer than yours, Dr. Robertson.") Only the experienced OR nurses are familiar with Dr. Robertson's idiosyncrasies, and on this particular morning it is a new-to-the-job circulating nurse that is teamed with a sleep-deprived Tomlinson — not a good combination.

From the first stroke of the scalpel Tomlinson falls two steps behind, and never catches up. Yet somehow, she muddles through without a major uproar, until it's time to close. Her relief at seeing the end is palpable. Then suddenly, her suture book is sailing across the room, and a furious Dr. Robertson is railing in exasperation, "Don't you know that I want my sutures cut twelve inches long?" he barks. "Did you read my standing orders, or is that too much to ask?" Then in a final cry of indignation, he glares at Tomlinson, and seethes, "Do you know how long twelve inches is?" "Yes sir," comes her startled reply. "It's a foot."

The next night Tomlinson is called again — a ruptured appendix — with the same Dr. Nasty. But this time she is ready for him, with sutures meticulously cut one foot long, and needles and sponges carefully counted and laid out in perfect order. She keeps one step ahead all the way to the final closure, avoiding flying missiles and cussings, but as Dr. Robertson is about to pull off his gloves, she makes the alarming discovery that a needle is missing. The cussing erupts after all. "Count again!" he demands, implying the error can only be hers. "I have counted twice, sir," she replies. "I am certain you did not hand me back the final needle." A little taken aback by the self-assurance of this student — and perhaps with the memory of her straightforward response the night before — he begins the search for the missing needle. Voila, it appears in the fold of a drape directly in front of him. He sheepishly hands it over... along with a chivalrous offer: "You can scrub for me any time, Miss Tomlinson." It was not the path Tomlinson would ultimately choose, but the offer was a great ego-booster.

I remember a similar experience scrubbing for Dr. W.O. Rothwell, the complete antithesis of Dr. St. Clair. Dr. Rothwell was a lovely, soft-spoken man, who treated us with kindness and respect, and we in turn adored him. The surgery had sailed along smoothly, and I was performing the final count as the last suture was being tied. One sponge short! *Gasp. I've counted wrong, but do I tell Dr. Rothwell now, or do I have time for a second count?* It's a terrible conundrum for anyone, but especially a junior student, even when working with a sympathetic surgeon. If a sponge is missing, it's imperative that he go back into the abdominal cavity to search for it. Imagine a simple counting error setting this in motion.

But all this counting is for good reason, and I cannot delay until the surgeon leaves, so I work up the courage. "Dr. Rothwell, I'm missing a sponge," I broach gingerly. "Are you sure, Miss King?" comes his patient reply. "I'll wait while you count again." Stretching each blood-soaked sponge out carefully, I repeat the count. Still one short. My heart is in my throat as Dr. Rothwell snips open all his handiwork and goes back in. We both heave a sigh when he draws out the elusive sponge. The unsuspecting patient never learned of his double operation, but I'm sure he would have been grateful that doctor and nurse did their job and he did not go home carrying a foreign body in his abdomen.

Dr. H. E. Gibson was as notorious as Dr. Robertson for throwing instruments that didn't meet his expectations. On one occasion, MacElheran was startled by a retractor flying over her shoulder, and her swift, instinctive response took everyone by surprise. "Don't you ever do that to me again,"she said, scowling in anger, her eyes meeting his in defiance. Then, realizing the audacity of her bold attack, she continued through the surgery in silence, nervously bracing for the reprimand she fully expected from her clinical instructor. Instead, she exited the operating room to the applause of the entire staff who had witnessed the now famous exchange. Nurse Braveheart would have recognized an ally.

Tigner recalls a vastly different encounter with Dr. Gibson. It took place during her obstetrics rotation, where she was to assist him with a delivery. Dr. Gibson's fearsome reputation had preceded him into the case room, and Tigner trembled uncontrollably as she scrubbed in preparation. As they passed the sink, the circulating staff kept filling her head with an alarming list of the good doctor's idiosyncrasies, until she was a complete wreck. Then the head nurse weighed in with one final warning: "Dr. Gibson usually delivers with forceps, and if you don't grab them immediately afterward, he will throw them." With *grab the forceps or he'll throw them*, running anxiously — and repeatedly — through her head, she breathlessly awaited the moment of truth. Then suddenly it was upon her: the babe's head was delivered, and Tigner had a split second to react. Still murmuring, *grab the forceps or he'll throw them*, she grabbed the forceps... and threw them! Jaws dropped in stunned disbelief. Tigner can scarcely believe her own story these fifty years later.

Peterson hasn't forgotten the charge nurse who strategized a plan to head off any Dr. Gibson nonsense before he got started. "I'm warning you right now, Dr. Gibson," she cautioned at the outset of a surgery, "one of your filthy jokes and my nursing staff will leave." All was calm as the surgery got underway; then suddenly Dr. Gibson broke the silence. "Did you hear the one about the prostitutes?" he smirked. The staff dropped everything and walked out. "Well, I can't tell it," he guffawed to their backs, "because they just left." Imagine his pleasure at trapping them in his lair.

Occasionally, we saw the softer side of Dr. Gibson — I call it his Sunday side. Sunday was the day he'd sometimes bring a little daughter on rounds, propping her up on the ledge of the desk while he examined charts. Even though he'd teasingly call her Nausea or Anorexia, she was clearly the apple of his eye. On one occasion, he entertained her by applying a cast around her wrist, and she went home beaming with delight over her beautiful new bracelet. Fully expecting he'd be able to soak it off at home before Anorexia's bedtime, it was a red-faced Dr. Gibson who turned up at Emergency late in the day to have it removed.

But we've not forgotten the doctors who treated us with respect — those who considered us partners on this journey, taking an interest in our education, whether formally in the classroom or as opportunity presented on the wards. Dr. McEwan stands out as one who fielded every question, always giving thoughtful, patient responses. Dr. Brown also springs to mind as a willing teacher; I never accompanied Dr. Brown on rounds without learning something new.

We were all in awe of Dr. Taylor, the quiet, serious, much loved, pioneer neurosurgeon, who used to read the nurses' notes attentively, claiming, "I can't be with my patients twenty-four hours a day. I trust the nurses to be my eyes and my ears." I thought of him when my father was admitted to the Psychiatric Ward in my senior year with a diagnosis of *anxiety disorder* — a loose term his doctor devised for lack of a more definitive label. One day a graduate nurse wrote on his chart, "Mr. King appears to walk with a Parkinson-like gait." An observant nurse had delivered a diagnosis.

I especially remember Dr. Taylor pulling me aside one evening when I was caring for his critically injured patient. "Miss King," he appealed, "I want you to record Mr. Stanley's vital signs as I have prescribed, but your observation of changes in his level of awareness will be more valuable to me." In the absence of today's technical paraphernalia, we were compelled to be keen observers, a practice our manageable caseloads and extended patient stays allowed.

We used to agonize over the number of losses Dr. Taylor experienced because of his particular specialty, and we wondered how he could soldier on with such grace and resolve. Peterson remembers a student once asking him if it wasn't a waste of his time and energy to remove a brain tumor when he knew death was imminent. "It's not a waste of time to give a patient more time with his family," he replied without hesitation, "or enough time to get his affairs in order." Another lesson from Dr. Taylor.

Some classmates remember Dr. Black for his down-to-earth, friendly demeanor. Tomlinson remembers a stiffer, more serious Dr. Black — one always immaculately dressed in a dark suit. She especially remembers the day in her senior year when she accompanied him on rounds with a junior student in tow. His patient, suffering a foot injury, was found sitting up in the sunroom with his foot propped on a stool. Dr. Black bent forward to examine the foot, then aiming to get a closer view from a seated position, he reached back between his legs for the chair behind him. With impeccable timing, the junior student decided the chair was in his way, so she pulled it back, and Dr. Black went sprawling. The fractured foot was now at perfect eye level for examining, but the doctor was busy attending his own shattered composure. He spurned Tomlinson's tenuous offer to help, so she escaped down the hall, leaving him to pat down his dark suit on his own. Staff at the desk had no clue what the hysterical laughter in the chart room was all about.

We giggled when Dr. Walker, the surgeon, tested us with his favorite joke — a request for a #6 safety pin. (The suggestion was that all safety pins are shaped like the number six.) He was also a bit of a flirt. And who could forget Dr. Noakes, the urologist with his bagful of quips befitting his specialty; or Dr. Corbet, the pediatrician with the gentle, reassuring hands; or Dr. Buchanan, the good-natured obstetrician, beloved by staff and patients alike. I remember a classmate asking the easy-going Dr. Buchanan what he thought of allowing fathers in the delivery room, an unheard-of circumstance at the time. He was quick to respond, "Definitely not! I've got my hands plenty full in there without having to worry about a fainting father." We barred the door when his wife was giving birth.

Meanwhile, Dr. Uptigrove, the intern, had his own set of problems in the case room. Thiessen recalls an unusually quiet night giving rise to an idle nursing staff restlessly pacing the floor hoping for some action. It also happened to be Dr. Uptigrove's last night on call, and it didn't seem right that he conclude his obstetric experience snoring in the call room. Their solution was to prepare

Annie, the practice doll, for delivery, and call their snoozing friend. "Dr. Uptigrove, come fast," pressed the charge nurse, "we have a woman fully dilated. She's about to deliver."

Dr. Uptigrove flew from his bed, and ran down the hall. Annie was in stirrups, draped, and moaning in agony, thanks to someone's Oscar-worthy voice-over performance. The frenzied intern began to scrub, but the charge nurse propelled him from the sink. "There's no time to scrub," she cried, "the head is crowning!" He flew to the delivery table and as the nurses encouraged Annie to "breathe," he grabbed the episiotomy scissors in readiness. It took a minute for him to process the fact that Annie wasn't quite anatomically equipped to deliver, before slinking out the door in embarrassed annoyance. As the beleaguered intern showered before catching another hour's sleep, the nurses decided they needed to make peace. Dr. Uptigrove returned to his sleeping quarters to the open arms of Annie waiting in his bed.

I wonder if Dr. Uptigrove ever shared this experience with fellow intern Dr. Mortis, who was similarly tested when on call for pediatrics. Any of us who worked on pediatrics when the new wing first opened remember the post-construction kitchen dwellers — the mice who travelled the pipes after dark. I remember them well, having played a significant role on the mouse patrol. Our charge nurse came to work one day armed with traps, which were effective, except only one staff member would empty them: me. No matter what my assigned shifts were, the mouse traps awaited my arrival. I loved arriving for work on pediatrics to the cheers of the entire staff: "Yeah, trap girl is here!" Unfortunately, Dr. Mortis did not receive such a welcome.

Fowler remembers the evening one little critter escaped the traps and terrorized the staff as it scurried about the ward. Finally, a couple of nurses, fed up with his intimidation, took after the little varmint with a large metal waste basket, cornering him in the kitchen where they whipped the inverted pail over him, trapping him beneath. Now, since they knew this type of trap was not in Miss King's job description, they put their heads together for a solution. A conveniently empty Room 13 offered one. They skidded the pail across the hall into the room and quietly closed the door. Then they went to the desk and paged, "Dr. Mortis, calling Dr. Mortis, please report to pediatrics — new admission in Room 13."

In the Heat of the Night

Many of us look back on our training days as three years of overwhelming fatigue from endless hours of work and study. Of course, we scheduled time for play, after which we were plumb out of hours for sleep, leaving us chronically deprived. That brings to mind the day Gertrude Hall spotted me slipping away in her *History of Nursing* class.

"Miss King, are you awake?" *Where is this voice coming from? Wha... where am I?* Then my head snaps and I realize it's the voice of Miss Hall straining above the class to address me, seated inconspicuously in the back corner of the room. *Inconspicuous, my foot. Nothing escapes Gertrude Hall. I'm in trouble.* Now that she has my attention, she rewords her question.

"Are you sleepy, Miss King?"

I have been to the brink of falling clean out of my desk, and she knows it, so what can I say except, "Yes, Miss Hall, I am a little sleepy." Then I brace for a grilling.

"Well then, class, it must be time for a ten minute break. Everybody up — move about. That's it — str-e-t-c-h." I was so shocked by this reprieve, I nearly fell out of my desk.

Fatigue was never more evident than when we worked nights — midnight to 8:00 a.m. — while the rest of the world slept. Since it was near impossible for our house mothers to monitor our varied sleep habits while on this shift, we occasionally took advantage of the situation with a day trip out of town, returning for the next night's shift with little or no sleep. Tomlinson remembers reporting for duty one night after sacrificing her eight hours of sleep for a day in Banff. The charge nurse, alert to the obvious fact that her stammering student was going to be of little use to her, trundled her off to an empty room and tucked her into bed for the night, waking her in time for morning report. We didn't always receive sympathy from those above us on the ladder; a sympathizer such as this was a true angel of mercy.

For many classmates, the shift of their inner clock was the culprit with night duty — they weren't lacking the good sense to get some sleep; their mind and body simply objected to the abnormal pattern of sleeping during the day and staying awake at night. I had no understanding of this; I could stay awake all night with ease and then zonk in the morning with a smile on my face. Rising at the crack of dawn was abnormal in my books, and it was my nemesis. (Fifty years later, nothing has changed.)

I loved working nights, especially in the winter when I could look from my post over to the residence at 6:00 a.m. and watch the lights snap on sporadically, room by room, floor by floor. *Those poor suckers*, I'd think to myself, *dragging themselves out of bed at this ungodly hour*. I didn't consider it inhumane to *be* up at that hour, but to *get* up at that hour was a whole different matter. That leads me to West Five, the diabetic ward; how I agonized for all those patients when I woke them every morning at 5:00 a.m. to collect a urine sample for testing. I often tried to put myself in the shoes of a diabetic; I speculated that I could adhere to diet restrictions reasonably well, and I could administer my own insulin injections with ease, but pee in a bottle at 5:00 a.m.? Not if my life depended on it!

Neufeld remembers her first shift of night duty, when she was dragging herself around. She had never been up at such hours in her entire life. By about 4:00 a.m. she simply could not keep her eyes open, so the charge nurse sent her into the chart room located behind the desk for a snooze. The next thing she knew, the orderly was shaking her awake with a warning that Black Mac, the supervisor, was on the unit. Not quite grasping the situation in her groggy state, she nevertheless recognized it was time to snap to and return to the job. With cap in hand she drifted out of the chart room yawning, "Boy, what a good sleep I had!" Suddenly it registered that a wide-eyed Black Mac was staring her in the face in disbelief. The charge nurse was quick to plead Neufeld's case, explaining that it was her student's first time on night duty and admitting she had given permission for the nap. There was no sawing wood in the chart room the next night, however.

The Eye, Ear, Nose and Throat (EENT) ward — a small unit on the main floor — especially comes to mind when we reminisce about night duty. It was the one place Gertrude Hall trusted to a lone senior student on nights — our first experience in charge. The responsibility for these patients was one thing, but sitting at that desk all alone in the dark was downright spooky. Every call bell that pierced the silence was jarring, and you grabbed your flashlight wondering what you were about to encounter.

Tonsillectomies worried us the most because of the potential, however uncommon, for hemorrhaging. Most of these patients were children, of course, and we made rounds from crib to crib shining our lights down throats every hour, while listening — and praying

— for our little charges to keep breathing until morning. Any child who'd experienced excessive bleeding on the day or evening shift had us nervously checking every ten minutes.

I was terrified the night the call light indicated the room of an eighty-six-year-old man recovering from cataract surgery. It was a time when the protocol for this surgery was to keep the patient still in bed for at least a week with eyes patched and head anchored with sand bags. My heart was pounding as I flew down the hall and into Mr. Squint's room, but I was relieved to find everything in apparent order. In fact, Mr. Squint is smiling and waving.

"Is that you nurse?" he croaks.

"Yes, Mr. Squint," I reply assuringly, "I'm here. Everything's just fine. You go back to sleep now." Then from under his pillow he extracts a five dollar bill and extends it in my direction.

"This is yours if you get under the covers with me," he proposes confidently, as if this is an offer I cannot refuse. I decline... but not without recognizing that this proposition is worth half my paycheque, albeit from a man four times my age, who doesn't know what I look like. Never mind — it will make a great story for a book one day.

No one told us there'd be days like this.

The swirling lights of the police and ambulance vehicles in the distance gave me advance warning, and I braced for my first emergency encounter. *A heart attack? Stroke? Maybe just a broken hip — at least I won't have to worry about that patient dying.* I took a deep breath, and talked to myself: *You can handle this; yes, you can.* Then the doors flew open, and in rolled a stretcher, manned, it seemed, by an army of burly attendants. The attendants were looking weary and impatient, and they were not conversing with their charge. Their demeanor as they hurriedly supplied the head nurse with the necessary information, gave me the sense that they could have been delivering a bag of laundry.

My first glimpse of Miss Black — viewed between the beefy shoulders of the attendants — horrified me. The poor soul was sitting upright on the stretcher, gathering a filthy, torn blanket about herself in an attempt to maintain some dignity. Her battered and swollen head wobbled above the ragged edge of the blanket. Then her eyes caught mine, and my heart stopped. I'll never forget those vacant eyes — windows to a missing soul. It was as though someone had stolen her very being from her.

I wheeled Miss Black into a cubicle, and as I peeled back her blanket, a life on the dark side unfolded — blood, bruises and black lace hanging in shreds. I heard my mother's voice — the hushed-tone voice — and I knew. This was the world she hoped I'd never have to encounter — a world light years from my world. Miss Black and I would have nothing in common. My world viewed a prostitute as the lowest of the low.

I tended to Miss Black's wounds with care, although not without silently passing judgement. We spoke little. We didn't get to know each other. It would take many years for me to learn that Miss Black and I had much in common: she was someone's daughter and so was I; someone's sister, and so was I. In the family of mankind, she was *my* sister. Our worlds were only just a hushed tone apart. Today, as she lives on in my memory, my heart goes out to her.

I ran the gamut of emotions on the Emergency Ward: fear, anger, joy, heartache, shock, despair, elation. Many times I couldn't define my emotion of the moment.

It was late Saturday afternoon, the wedding day of an ecstatic young couple south of town. Vows had been said, and the bride and groom, delirious with joy, were travelling from the church to the photographer's studio to capture their special day for all time, before welcoming family and friends at a reception. Their groomsman at the wheel glanced through the mirror and smiled with pleasure at the sight of his best friend embracing his radiant bride. None of them saw it coming. A carload of drunken revellers ran a red light and hit them broadside. The stunning satin wedding gown became a river of red. I never considered myself a Harlequin Romance kind of girl, but like any single twenty-year-old, I might have confessed to the occasional daydream of a prince charming, a white wedding, and happily ever after. Yet here I was, witnessing such a day evolve into an unthinkable nightmare.

I remember caring for the bride in one room, while the groom was attended to across the hall. The bride kept slipping in and out of lucidity, and each time the fog lifted, she asked about her new husband. Then she'd lose touch, and the cycle would repeat. When she finally emerged from her state of shock to a more stable condition, she became convinced that her husband was dead; that I was cushioning her from the unthinkable truth. The solution was obvious; I wheeled her stretcher across the hall and wedged it into the small, crowded room where he lay fighting for his life. Even in their imperilled state, they instinctively reached out to one another from their respective stretchers. I can still see the two of them in their torn and bloodied, formal wedding attire, their gripped hands holding onto life itself. They both miraculously survived, and I have never forgotten them. How often I have prayed that after their horrifying beginning they found a happily-ever-after ending.

My other lasting memory of Emergency was the day Huckleberry Finn came calling. It was a sunny day in July, and a neighborhood boy — perhaps eight years old — had been fishing in the nearby Bow River, when he unexpectedly landed the catch of his life. Apparently, he got a bit too much action on his fly rod, and the hook flew back and snagged him just above his upper lip. Tough guys don't run home to Mother, he decided; what could she do about this anyway? (Maybe tough guys also don't want Mother to see them with a fly hook on their face.) In any event, since there was a hospital in plain sight, what could be simpler than going direct?

The sight of this little waif coming up the driveway in rolled-up pants and dusty bare feet, fishing rod slung over his shoulder and a feather moustache leaping from his dirty face was something to behold. We removed his moustache, and I don't remember if a family member came to collect him, although someone surely did. I do remember thinking that this tough little guy and his fishing rod would assuredly be back down on the riverbank at the crack of dawn the next morning.

The Psychiatric Ward, a dark, depressing place in the hospital basement (B West) is well remembered by the classmates who received their psychiatric experience there rather than at the Provincial Hospital in Ponoka. For many, memories of the lockup unit spring to mind first when they look back to their time on B West. Ward's lockup story tickled the funny bone of a *Calgary Herald* cartoonist, who took great pleasure in ridiculing the local police force.

It seems two of Calgary's plain clothes detectives had been recruited to transport a suspected mental patient charged with a criminal offense to the General's psychiatric ward. The three men were greeted by an orderly and directed to a lockup room into which the two officers accompanied their charge. After the first officer left the room, the patient quickly followed him out, and called for the orderly to lock the door on the remaining party. The orderly swiftly obliged. Confusion reigned as the first officer set chase after his fleeing charge while his locked-up partner cussed a blue streak that could be heard in Balzac.

"Heh! Heh! Rather an odd illusion — imagines himself a policeman."

Hill tells of receiving a late-night visit from a security guard mystified by a pile of goods that had appeared outside on the south lawn below B West just since he last made rounds. Aware that the windows, designed to obstruct escapes, were not much larger than the slot in a letter box, Hill nevertheless examined each room with her flashlight. Lo and behold, she discovered a patient who, unable to escape himself, was gleefully doing the next best thing; he was painstakingly feeding every single item in the room that would fit through the slot out into the night. By now, everything but the

Cartoon: Tom Innes, Calgary Herald, circa. 1958

mattress — clothing, books, toiletries, towels, sheets — lay in a pool on the lawn, outlined by the glow of the moon.

Friday night on B West was entertainment night for the patients, the students being responsible for coming up with recreation ideas. Matthews was lucky; her father was freshly into square dancing, a perfect diversion for her Friday assignment. It took little coaxing for her to bring him on board. Mr. Matthews arrived early in hat and boots, and set about preparing the music and the mic for the evening's calls, while his daughter organized her patients into squares.

One woman, known to suffer extreme mood swings, shuffled unwillingly into place, not the least pleased with her forced participation. When the music began, however, Miss Dosidoe's depression lifted, and she became the life of the party. That became a problem when she took a fancy to the handsome caller and whirled indiscreetly round and round him. It took all Mr. Matthews' concentration to continue with the evening's calls while dodging his admirer. His daughter was unsure whether to expose her amusement or not.

Sidelines

Two unique areas that turned up in our rotation experience were the Diet Kitchen (DK) – four dreary weeks of drawing up dreadfully dull special menus and assembling diabetic packs; and the Central Supply Room (CSR), where we hobbled off duty every day for two weeks with our legs screaming in pain from standing on an unforgiving basement floor all day, assembling treatment trays.

Who today would believe the proceedings in the CSR fifty years ago, where every salvageable piece of equipment was meticulously washed, examined, and recycled? Disposable was not in our vocabulary. Imagine soaking all the used needles, then standing them on a centrifugal machine that whirled out any residual fluid. Before they went into the autoclave for sterilizing, we performed one final step, my favorite. We'd gently run a finger along the point of the needle feeling for barbs, which we'd sand off on a stone as required. Good for yet another shot. I still shudder at the size of the needles we used to administer molasses-thick penicillin. Syringes, of course, were likewise soaked, washed and sterilized for reuse.

Rubber gloves were washed, turned, tested for holes, wrapped and sent through the autoclave along with catheters that had received similar attention. The most time-consuming tasks were piecing together specific trays for every sterile procedure performed in the hospital, from inserting a catheter, to changing a dressing or aspirating a joint. Each tray had a photo card outlining the instruments required and their layout, and there was no end to these elaborate trays. The entire tray was wrapped in heavy green linens before sterilization.

When I had a total hip replacement a few years ago, I chuckled at the memory of our fancy dressing trays. My nurse arrived on my first day post-op, ripped the dressing from my long incision in one quick swipe, and sent me into the shower. No dressing tray required. Nor was a suture removal tray required; I went home on the fourth day wearing my tidy row of clamps.

The Diet Kitchen was in a world of its own, and my memory of time spent there is vague. I do remember drawing up completely unimaginative menus that included salt-free butter, salt-free bread, salt-free soup for anyone on a salt-free diet. Low-salt diets called for low-salt butter, low-salt bread, low-salt soup... How easy was that? Similarly, every item on the diabetic diet was sugar-free and fat-free (FF), except that everything had to be weighed in grams:

Roast beef	60
FF peas	100
FF mashed potato	100
FF yellow beans	100
Bread	30
Butter	5
Skim milk	120
Diabetic pineapple	80

Only recently, I learned from Finch that her worst nightmare had been delivering the diet carts to their rightful locations throughout the hospital; she perpetually lost her way. To think that I had painstakingly filled all those diabetic packs only to have Finch lose them on some elevator.

But there was an obvious upside to working in the diet kitchen — the proximity to food, a precious commodity. Expanding girths were a telltale indication of those on DK rotation. I remember two occasions when I dipped into forbidden goods — probably because I was stung both times. The first was the day I frothed up a concoction for tube feedings — a healthy mixture of vitamins and minerals that took on the look of a yummy milkshake, an item that certainly never appeared on our menu. I filled all the required containers as ordered, and danced on the counter when there was a glass left over. It's amazing how your brain can go soft when you're salivating. I popped a straw into my chocolate shake and drew up the most vile tasting stuff imaginable. I was infuriated. The deception of my imagined drink was one thing, but what can be said about my embarrassing stupidity? I made the thing; I knew there was no ice cream, no chocolate, no sugar in it. I knew that palatability was not considered in the preparation of feedings going directly into the stomach. What a colossal dummy.

Red-handed in the pastry fridge.

The second occasion was just as disappointing, but I plead ignorance on this one — there's no way I could have known. One of the fads in high school was to cut the corner off a Jell-O powder box, then tap the powder into your mouth throughout the day for a sugar fix as desired. M-m-m. We wore the flavor of the day on our red, green or yellow grins. One day when I was putting the remnants of my shift into the hospital pantry, I struck gold — a whole bin of Jell-O powder! I filled a paper cup with my contraband, squashed it shut, stuffed it into my bib, and dashed for my room. Locking my door — I wasn't about to share my windfall with anyone — I shed my uniform, kicked off my shoes, and curled up on my bed eager for a lick of the flavor of the day, its purple hue suggesting grape. In went my tongue... argh-h-h! If I thought the tube feeding was bad, this was rat poison. Then I got to wondering if it really was rat poison. I never had the courage to seek out information about what this stuff really was; I am only grateful I survived to confess the story.

Personal Trainers

My classmates and I are quick to recognize our good fortune in having been mentored by the best — a string of exceptional directors, instructors and senior staff nurses who coached us through our three-year education with their knowledge and skills and set impressive examples of dedication to the profession. Only one sister reported her memory of a graduate nurse who made a long-standing impression in a negative way — a grad whose perceived importance barred her from getting into the trenches with students who were taxed beyond the limit on a particular evening shift. "I told myself I would never be this kind of nurse when I graduated," vowed my classmate who experienced this occasion, "and I never was." Thankfully, the single-minded grad nurse is on a list of one. We have a much longer list of those who left a favorable impression.

Miss White taught us not to sweat the small stuff. She's the one who stressed care over castors. Miss Barker's unmistakable humanity and genuine love of nursing and teaching was a profound influence on any who passed through her hands. And not one of us would forget Mrs. Wheatley, the highly educated and skilled instructor on Neurology, who oversaw students and patients alike with an eagle eye. How I remember her pounding into our heads the importance of treating the comatose patient as though he or she were fully cognizant, because we just never know. I'll admit I raised my eyebrows the day I saw her demonstrate her philosophy to the letter, chatting on about the weather to a totally unresponsive patient as she expertly cared for all his needs. There was an air of absurdity about it to me at the time. Then I had my own firsthand experience.

I was assigned the care of Mr. Blue, the victim of a traffic accident that came within a whisker of taking his life. He had stepped off a sidewalk into the path of a city bus, the question of intent remaining unanswered. My task was to provide the physical and emotional support he needed for full recovery. My charge nurse assigned me to Mr. Blue every day that first week to maintain continuity of care, a significant aid to recognizing changes in the patient's level of awareness. The entire week, however, Mr. Blue remained in a deep coma, entirely unresponsive to the conversation that I was providing as prescribed by Mrs. Wheatley. Wavering now and then about the validity of talking to my charge in such a condition, I nevertheless followed my instructor's lead, as I greeted him daily with a cheery, "Good morning Mr. Blue. I'm Miss King, and I'm going to be your nurse again today." Then, while rubbing his back, I'd impose a litany of complaints on him about the unfairness of all the rules in my residence, before droning on for the rest of my shift, spewing unimportant drivel about the life of a student nurse. He must have been more relieved than I was when I had a day off.

When I reported back for duty the following morning, I learned that Mr. Blue had regained consciousness in my absence. I bounded into his room in excitement.

"Good morning, Mr. Blue," I said enthusiastically. "What's this I hear about you?"

"Good morning," he said, beaming, "you're Miss King."

"Wha...? How do you know that?"

"I recognize your voice," he replied, matter-of-factly. I trusted Mrs. Wheatley's every dictate from that day forward.

Mrs. Brigden, in charge of the small eight-bed Isolation Unit, was a sterling example of a nurse finely tuned to the needs — and the fears — of her patients... and her students. She was extremely knowledgeable in her specialty, and cared for everyone with intelligence, warmth and understanding. Students had an understandable fear of contracting the communicable diseases that confronted them on this unit, and Mrs. Brigden's magical touch quickly dispelled their fears. Two of our sisters — Link and Kell — had the good fortune (or arguably, the bad luck) to experience Mrs. Brigden's touch on their first day as students, when they were sent to her loving arms almost before they had unpacked.

It all began with Link's close circle of family and friends in Medicine Hat embracing her with farewell hugs and kisses throughout the week leading up to her departure for Calgary. Buried in their hugs was a case of mumps that erupted the day she arrived. Kell quickly succumbed, and the two were secluded in Isolation before their mushrooming faces spread to the rest of us. It was not how they had envisioned their first three weeks as student nurses, but Mrs. Brigden brought some measure of comfort. Isolation was also frequently home to a string of sad, innocent waifs abandoned by parents who retrieved them only at their own whim.

The head nurse on Pediatrics, Mrs. Currie, stands out as one of the best in Tigner's memory. "That woman considered every child her own," she recalls, "and how I remember the exercise of collecting the line-up of dirty diapers, then standing before her to accurately describe the color, odor and consistency of their contents."

Tomlinson is quick to name Mrs. Donaldson, her clinical instructor on Gynecology, as the one who unequivocally turned on the light for her — the one who gave her the inspiration that she could actually be a nurse. She was drawn to Mrs. Donaldson's philosophy of listening to one's instincts — of believing that if something doesn't *feel* right, then it probably isn't. She also embraced Mrs. Donaldson's principle of never asking someone to do something you're not willing to do yourself.

Those who went to Ponoka remember Miss Sunberg, who set an example of respect and compassion for all her patients —both the troubled and the troublesome — who were spurned by the rest of the world.

And last, but not least, not one of us will ever forget Miss Macdonald — the Calgary General Hospital's famous "Black Mac," the fearless (and fearsome) night supervisor who dedicated her

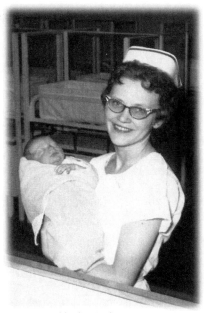

Newbies in the nursery

life to her career. Thiessen remembers the night she was alone in the obstetric nursery, working herself into a flap over her impossible caseload. An unrelenting chorus of crying babies was a constant reminder of her predicament. She saw Black Mac arriving on rounds, and braced herself for a reprimand. Instead, the unflappable supervisor assessed the situation, assured herself a life was not at risk, and simply commiserated. "Do the best you can," she said, then continued on her way.

My memory of Black Mac was a night on Emergency when back-to-back car accidents had created chaos. Stretchers spilled out of every room into the hallways. The charge nurse had made frantic but unsuccessful attempts to locate beds throughout the hospital so that the most serious cases could be admitted. In despair, she paged Black Mac. Within minutes, the double doors of the Emergency Ward crashed open, and the imposing figure of this towering woman advanced down the hall. Her eyes scanned the scene, darting from stretcher to stretcher. Then she pulled the chart of the patient she assessed the most critical, tucked it under her arm, and marched to the phone. She dialed Neurology. "I am sending a Mr. Shock for admission," she announced firmly. I could hear a muffled reply; "But we don't have an available bed, Miss Macdonald." "Well, then, *get* one," she roared, and hung up. On the thankfully few occasions in recent years that I have found myself in the nightmare of a gridlocked emergency ward, a situation seemingly beyond anyone's power to resolve, I think of Black Mac. No bed? Well, *get* one.

Peterson remembers the uncanny ability of our microbiology teacher, Mrs. Dahlstrom, to coolly deliver the day's lesson, all the while writing the notes for tomorrow's lesson on the blackboard. Personally, I was far too consumed with grasping the rudiments of the course to observe such trickery. Meanwhile, Langford embraces warm thoughts of the cool Mrs. Dahlstrom. Observing that Langford, a California girl, was desperately homesick during those early days, she took her under her wing, and on more than one occasion, brought her home for tea and conversation after classes. Mrs. Dahlstrom's friend, Miss Jordan, was similarly known to befriend a lonely student on occasion. Thiessen has never forgotten her supper invitation from Miss Jordan, capped with an evening at the Ice Capades. It kept her gliding for weeks.

Someone who holds a special place in my heart is the spirited charge nurse on North Three with the sweet Irish brogue. How I wish I could remember her name. She was a wee thing with a heart as big as a house. I was assigned North Three through the Christmas season of my third year, a Christmas I would be celebrating without the company of a single member of my immediate family. My parents and elder brother were in California, where Mother was in the grip of a debilitating depression. My other brother, confronted with these circumstances, elected to remain in Vancouver where he was enrolled at UBC.

When Mrs. Ireland learned of my situation, I might as well have been a lost war orphan, in her eyes. "I'll be just fine," I assured her, "I'm working the day shift anyway, as you know, and my aunt has invited me for dinner." But then I lost my resolve to be really noble, and confessed that my one and only gift from my California Santa was in the clutches of Canada Customs, and I had no way to retrieve it in view of my duty schedule. Mrs. Ireland was horrified. She fussed the rest of the shift. Then at 3:00 p.m., a full hour before our shift ended, she gathered her purse and steered me toward the elevator.

"Run and change, Miss King. We're going to Customs."

"Oh, that's not necessary, Mrs. Ireland," I stammered in disbelief. "I, er, I, I'm... "

"I'll decide what's necessary," she declared, propelling me into the elevator and pressing the tunnel button. And that's how Santa delivered my gift that year.

I reported for duty Christmas morning to a ward operating with a skeleton staff, which was adequate for the low bed count. Mrs. Ireland assigned a young woman to my care — a woman my own age, who was in kidney failure. She had been married less than a year, and this was her first Christmas with her husband, who was attending her around the clock. Mrs. Ireland, heartsick with the situation confronting this young couple, freed me of all duties outside their care, so that I could offer the comfort and attention they needed throughout the day.

Christmas that year was tranquility in a quiet room with three young innocents sharing dreams, fears and beliefs. I could not answer the pleading eyes of that despairing husband; I could not save his wife — she died mid-afternoon — but in the absence of the usual distractions of Christmas, I could give myself to them without reservation. I don't look back on that Christmas as a lonely one, or a sad one; I remember it as the year the spirit of Christmas was truly alive. The day was a gift to me.

Memories Are Made of This

Three unique encounters as a student nurse left indelible imprints on me. Their endings differ: the first is unknown to me; the second promises some sketchy pieces of information; and the third reached its conclusion on my watch. The first story centres around my first marriage proposal.

Gerald was a handsome redhead with a dazzling smile. He was sweet and smart and generous of spirit — a catch, in anyone's books. He popped the question quite unexpectedly, as I was fussing about his bed, performing the finishing touches. "Miss King, will you marry me?" he asked, clear out of the blue. Just like that. No preamble. Straight to the point. My heart skipped a beat, as I considered my answer. "Oh Gerald," I replied forlornly, "if only you were a little older, I'd marry you for sure." Gerald was crestfallen and hung his head in despair. I gave it a pat, and assured him that I was moved by his proposal. Then I had to get on with my day, and leave this sad little twelve-year-old to sort out his feelings of rejection.

I returned to Gerald's room an hour later carrying his lunch tray, fully expecting to encounter the same sad face I had last seen. Instead, I found a little boy bursting with excitement — eyes flashing as he breathlessly awaited my arrival. "Miss King," he chirped enthusiastically, stopping me in my tracks, "if I grow up real fast, then will you marry me?" He had worked out the perfect solution, yet I had to dash his dream a second time. "Oh dear, Gerald," I sighed, "I just don't think you can grow up fast enough."

At one time or another, we all encountered Barb and Johnny, two unforgettable, long-term residents of West Six, whose circumstance broke our hearts. Barb and Johnny were the victims of polio, a monster that was robbing them of their best years, stealing their limbs and paralyzing the chest muscles that were vital to their breathing. They were sealed in iron lungs, huge, hissing machines that kept them alive with intermittent positive pressure breathing. When the air was pumped out of their cylinder, reduction in pressure made their chests rise, filling the lungs. When the air was allowed back in, the lungs would empty. I often wondered how they slept with the constant whooshing of the machines, but they were known to remark that the sound was music to their ears.

I have a clear memory of learning about the iron lungs in the classroom, having, for some inexplicable reason, jumped at the opportunity to be the guinea pig for our instructor's demonstration. I popped inside the long metal tube, and stuck my head out the end, feeling like a magician's assistant about to be sawed in half. Then Miss Fryer plugged in the machine, and whoosh... an elephant sat on my chest as the air rushed in. Then it released, and my chest rose, bringing blessed relief... before the next elephant sat down. The initial sensation was unnerving since, without impaired chest muscles, I found myself at loggerheads with the machine, fighting to breathe in when it was bent on my breathing out. I had to concentrate on surrendering to its will. I also discovered I could only speak during the *out* cycle, a simple fact of life that it took an iron lung to point out to me.

We all entered the iron lung room on West Six with trepidation the first time. What if the equipment breaks down? What if the power goes off? Will the auxiliary generators really kick in? Today? I was thankful we'd been carefully instructed in how to manually operate the iron lungs in such an event, but I was doubly thankful

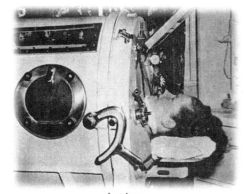

Iron lung

the manual operation was never required. Barb and Johnny could have rested assured, however, that one blip of a power outage would have brought two hundred fifty student nurses running from every corner of the hospital.

Barb was a young mother of four girls, who'd been wrenched from her cherished role as guide and nurturer to her daughters. She had beautiful blonde hair flowing from her headrest, and she was eternally gracious and kind. Thinking about her today still brings tears to my eyes. Murray remembers taking Barb's girls home to the Murray farm in High River on a day off once. Murray's mother met the train. The girls had the time of their lives riding the horse and chasing the chickens. Murray praises Barb's devoted husband who stood by his wife's side, while raising their girls with her wise counsel. Outside connections such as Murray's were not uncommon amongst staff members who embraced patients as family, with the extended families of both parties forming strong bonds.

Johnny was a strapping young guy who hailed from Lethbridge, a promising junior hockey star, whose thrill of the ice now lived only in his dreams. He was just nineteen years old, playing hockey for Great Falls, Montana, when he was stricken with polio during a game in Medicine Hat in December of 1953 — the year of the infamous scourge. Now he ran a business from his room, selling white duty stockings by special order. He had the market cornered.

Barb and Johnny required total care, their bathing, skin care, exercise, and toileting made possible through portals in the iron lungs. They were at our mercy for every last thing, from feeding to turning the pages of a book anchored above their head. I tried to imagine the frustration of receiving a mouthful of potatoes when your taste buds were revved up for the corn, or reading a page-turner novel, when you couldn't turn the page... or watching the world pass by through an overhead mirror.

Barb and Johnny were transferred to Edmonton in 1960, a move designed to consolidate all the province's thirty-five iron lungs under one roof, where patients could receive specialized therapy to wean them from the iron lungs and maximize their potential. Barb and Johnny faced the upheaval heroically, but parting with these beloved family members was great trauma for their caregivers on West Six. They were quickly adopted, however, by their new family on Unit 67 of the University Hospital in Edmonton.

Johnny, already using a rocking bed for periods each day while in Calgary, soon adapted to life outside the iron lung as he continued to use the rocking bed and a portable respirator. He took up mouth painting to help fill the hours, and produced some pleasing works. Then on January 28, 1962, at the age of twenty-eight, he died suddenly and unexpectedly from a ruptured cerebral aneurysm. Gary McPherson was a hospital mate of Johnny's at the time. In Gerald W. Hankins' biography of McPherson, *Rolling On*, McPherson was quoted as saying, "Johnny escaped the long years of disability that lay before him." It was Gary McPherson's sense that Johnny would have welcomed this reprieve from a destiny of dependence.

Barb had a tougher time shedding the iron lung, as she learned in stages to make use of a respirator and breathe for short periods on her own. In a year's time, her doctors deemed her ready to return to Calgary and her awaiting family. Katarina DeFrain, a beloved caregiver, remembers well the day that she had to say good-bye to her dear friend. Taking a day off work without pay, she accompanied Barb on the trip to Calgary, making certain she was safely settled into her own sunny little room at the Baker Sanatorium. Katarina and Barb corresponded for a few years, then the letters slowed, and eventually the two friends lost touch. Katarina regrets that Barb disappeared from her life, but she has never forgotten her. Barb's Calgary General family has never forgotten her either.

Another long-term patient during our tenure was Mrs. Kay, an elderly victim of a stroke that left her in a coma, entirely unresponsive to stimulation of any kind. Day after day, month after month, she lay in this state on North Six, seemingly in another world. Like Barb and Johnny, she was dependent on us for her total care — bathing, turning, feeding — but there were no mashed potatoes for her, just (foul-tasting) tube feedings. We heeded Mrs. Wheatley's dictate at all times, treating Mrs. Kay with utmost respect, and conversing with her as though she were fully cognizant of us and of her surroundings.

I can still see her devoted husband, arriving the same time every morning to spend the day at her side, lovingly offering little niceties — washing her face, combing her hair, massaging her neck, rubbing her feet — while filling her in on the events of their hours apart since his last visit. He travelled by city bus, and as assuredly as the sun came up, he could be counted on to appear at the same bus stop, at the same hour every single day.

Then one day, the sun did not come up. At staff report that morning, our charge nurse shared heartbreaking news that she had just received about Mr. Kay; he had died suddenly of a heart attack the previous evening. She now faced the unenviable task of informing his beloved wife. We all wondered, would this information register with her? We didn't dispute, however, that it was our moral duty to deliver the terrible news. And so, our charge nurse approached the bedside, took Mrs. Kay's hand in hers, and gently told her that Mr. Kay would not be visiting today... nor the next. A tear rolled down Mrs. Kay's cheek. She died within forty-eight hours. I experienced a startling neurology lesson that day, but more significantly, I received a life lesson. I had witnessed a love story that, for me, remains unrivalled to this day.

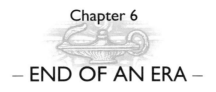

– END OF AN ERA –

Nursing Education Takes a New Path

Throughout my training days, there was never a moment when I did not feel the hand of Gertrude Hall on my shoulder — presiding over my every move, as I faltered along in a loyal attempt to prove my worth and discharge her bidding. I'm ashamed to admit, however, that I gave little thought to the possibility that her world extended beyond the four walls she shared with us students. The fact of the matter is, Gertrude Hall was perpetually in motion behind the scenes, occupied with the larger picture of the nursing profession.

In spite of the fact that she herself had not pursued formal education beyond a certificate in public health, Miss Hall was an ardent champion of higher education for nurses, and she began her crusade at home. She constantly sought funding to send CGH graduates to other hospitals for clinical training in specialized areas such as neurosurgery, urology, orthopedics or psychiatry, with the intention that they pass their new knowledge and skills on to staff and students on their respective wards. She also encouraged her clinical instructors and head nurses to seek university courses that would enhance their teaching and supervision skills.

It had been Miss Hall's practice throughout her career to network with national and provincial hospital associations in order to examine issues affecting nurses and nursing. In fact, it was through her network of contacts that Dr. Bradley first discovered her, and subsequently engaged her as Director of Nursing at the Calgary General. Throughout her eight-year tenure in this position, she was actively involved in nursing education provincially, serving on the education committee of the Alberta Association of Registered

Nurses (AARN). It's not surprising that Miss Hall's educational connections led to an affiliation between the CGH School of Nursing and the University of Alberta degree program. This affiliation began under her direction in the fall of 1954, a time when the U of A administered a branch in Calgary, which offered introductory courses in arts, science, commerce and engineering.

The five-year degree program consisted of one year of general science at the U of A, at either the Edmonton or Calgary campus; three years regular nursing training at either the U of A Hospital or the Calgary General Hospital; and a fifth year of either public health or teaching and supervision, offered only at the U of A Edmonton campus. Interestingly, even though Miss Hall was a huge supporter of degree education, she became increasingly dissatisfied with this program, arguing that it was unnecessarily long and educationally unsound.

In an April 28, 1959 memorandum to Dr. Crosby Johnston, Hall identified two main weaknesses in the program:

1. There was a disassociation between the three-year clinical portion, which fell outside the jurisdiction of the university, and the other two years, which were under its control. She contended that this set-up was educationally flawed. Instead, the clinical experience should be an integral part of the program, planned and directed by the university faculty, with equal emphasis on social, preventative and curative aspects of nursing.

2. The objectives of the university setting and the clinical setting differed. The university degree was designed to prepare nurses for leadership positions in the fields of public health or teaching and supervision, and therefore its entire curriculum should focus on this objective. Conversely, the three-year clinical portion of the program was designed for hospital nurse-training, focusing on hospital care and curative aspects of illness.

Miss Hall contended that a four-year integrated, controlled program would be more sensible; it would produce the best possible leaders in nursing in the shortest time consistent with sound education. Her ultimate goal was to remove nursing education from hospital control and establish it fully in the mainstream educational system. Yet Gertrude Hall may have unwittingly been keeping one foot in the way of her own goal. Early nurse training schools, grounded in the gendered ideology of women's role in society, often focused on discipline and character above all else. Miss Hall was one of the first directors to structure a model that separated education from service, but she still embraced a "pink book" mentality that accompanied us throughout our three years training. Some nurse historians have suggested that training "virtue" was a major factor in hindering the advancement of nursing education in a largely male-dominated academic world. Yet one of the nursing profession's early allies was a male.

George M. Weir, Federal Minister of Education, conducted a national study of nursing education from 1929-1931, reporting his findings in 1932. Weir stated that nursing education was in an appalling state, and strongly suggested that authority for operating schools of nursing should lie within the educational system, not under hospital jurisdiction. He was quick to recognize, for example, that scheduling 62% of classes in the first year was not in the best interest of the student; clearly the motive was to prepare her as quickly as possible to serve the needs of the hospital. "The fallacy of cramming the student nurse by giving her two-thirds of her classroom instruction in the first third of her training," he wrote, "is too obvious to require extended comment." Release of the revolutionary *Weir Report* on nursing education created quite a stir in the medical and educational community, but regrettably, all the talk it initiated did not lead to action. Little change took place for two decades.

Helen E. M. Penhale, Director of the University of Alberta School of Nursing from 1946 to 1956 was the first Alberta nursing educator to move toward changing the five-year non-integrated degree program to a four-year integrated curriculum. Using a 1942 University of Toronto pilot project model, she implemented her program at U of A in 1952. Within a year, Dr. Angus McGugan, the Superintendent of the Hospital, delivered its death knell. At a special meeting of the University Hospital Board, he outlined the difficulties he foresaw concerning the dual role of the Director of Nursing, now answerable to both the the Hospital Board and the University's Board of Governors. He recommended a return to the previous school arrangement. The Hospital Board approved his recommendation, and the U of A Board of Governors concurred. The AARN failed to intervene, perhaps because its main spokesperson was Penhale herself, its president during the transition. In 1954, the previous five-year program was reinstated.

Janet Ross-Kerr, in her book *Prepared to Care,* suggests that the termination of this first integrated baccalaureate program was "an example of a situation in which a leading nursing administrator was prevented from acting in ways designed to serve the public and the profession better." The battle for change was waged on many fronts, beginning with the widespread attitude that education for women — especially married women — was not valued as highly as education for men. Unfortunately, divisions also existed within the profession itself. All too frequently, diploma instructors viewed the integrated model as competitive and were disinclined to promote it.

In spite of this history of a failed four-year integrated program at the U of A, Gertrude Hall continued to attack the five-year "sandwich" program, openly voicing disapproval of its director, Ruth McClure (successor to Helen Penhale), who fiercely supported it.

Hall felt especially justified in arguing the disassociation between the two portions of the program — the educational and the practical — in the face of McClure's almost total lack of interest in the university's clinical affiliation with Hall's school of nursing. McClure made only rare, cursory visits to CGH, and not a single member of her faculty ever appeared on site, providing strong evidence of their disinterest and unfamiliarity with three-fifths of their own degree program.

Hall was also keenly aware of the high attrition rate — the number of students dropping out after their clinical experience, impatient to begin salaried positions. Now finding it increasingly difficult to counsel candidates into the U of A's five-year program — one she no longer embraced — Hall requested a conference with McClure; Jeanie Clark, Director of Nursing Service at the U of A Hospital; and Walter Johns, President of the U of A. Dr. Crosby Johnston accompanied Hall to add his voice to the controversy. The meeting was held in Edmonton on June 17, 1959. To think — that this was taking place as I was approaching my own graduation! I had no clue. I'm flabbergasted.

Hall first presented the issue of entrance requirements — senior matriculation — established in the original U of A/CGH affiliation agreement. Due to a drop in enrolment, the CGH School of Nursing had, out of necessity, dropped its entrance requirements, calling only for a high school diploma. Hall maintained that this lowered entry standard created a problem with the five-year program as structured. Degree students who had completed a year of studies at university level were now dropped back into a clinical program designed for students arriving directly from high school, many of whom lacked a senior matriculation. Hall saw this lumping together of the two groups as bad for the morale of the degree students. Yet still, she received no support for the four-year program she sought. Reluctantly, she suggested a compromise: that one U of A instructor be assigned to supervise the CGH degree students during their practical experience, and that those students be offered an enriched program.

These proposals were rejected by all three U of A representatives at the table. McClure and Clark stood firm in their opposition to revise the five-year segmented degree program, arguing that in a four-year program, students would not receive enough practical experience. When no compromise could be reached, McClure and Clark further recommended that the CGH affiliation with U of A be discontinued. All parties agreed to a temporary interruption. In January, 1960, the affiliation was formally discontinued. No further degree students entered the CGH School of Nursing for their second year after that date.

Gertrude Hall might well have used Queen Elizabeth II's famous expression "annus horribilis" to describe the year 1960 in her extensive nursing career. Having conceded defeat in the long battle for revision of the nursing degree program, she and her faithful compatriot, Dr. Crosby Johnston, also lost the battle for more funding for the hospital. In fact, City Council not only turned down their request for funding, it voted to cut twelve graduate nurse positions, including that of residence director of the school. Hall was despondent over this action, fearing it would lead to the hospital's reverting to its former practice of relying on students for its labor force. Such a situation would compromise the nursing program she had fought so hard to achieve. Even more troubling to her was the inevitable jeopardy to patient care that she foresaw.

An embattled Gertrude Hall handed in her resignation, effective October 31, 1960, and accepted a call from Toronto Sick Children's Hospital to survey its nursing personnel and its patient care needs in preparation for a redesign of its nursing department. Sadly, she did not live to attend this call. She died in Calgary on October 14, graduation night for the Class of '60. To the medical staff who had supported her efforts, she left behind one final counsel: "Mediocrity in health service cannot be condoned, and the health professions have a responsibility to interpret the needs of patients to all levels of government, and to the general public."

Gertrude Hall had taken an institution on the decline, and in the course of eight years, transformed it into a proud and vital centre. Yet her aspirations for the Calgary General to become the premier teaching hospital for the University of Calgary's future Faculty of Medicine would never be realized. At the time of Hall's death, a new hospital was on the affluent provincial government's drawing board. The Foothills Hospital opened in 1966, the same year the Calgary Branch of the University of Alberta reached autonomy. The General continued to maintain standing as a teaching institution, but the Foothills would claim the coveted honor as the premier teaching facility for the new University of Calgary's Faculty of Medicine, launched in 1970. Additionally, the status of the Foothills as a provincial hospital allowed the provincial government to maintain administrative control. When the Rockyview Hospital opened the same year, the seemingly aged Calgary General slipped further from prominence. Enrolment in its nursing school dwindled as large numbers of candidates were attracted to the Foothills' large new diploma program and Mount Royal College's pioneer two-year program. The General's School of Nursing was forced to close its doors in 1974. The Holy Cross Hospital School of Nursing followed suit five years later. But the battle to move all nursing programs into the educational system waged on.

On the national front throughout my training years, Helen Mussallem, a British Columbia nursing educator, was backing

Gertrude Hall with her own crusade for better nursing education. In 1957 Mussallem was selected by the Canadian Nurses' Association to direct a pilot project to evaluate nursing schools across the country to determine their readiness for a program of national voluntary accreditation. Criteria included philosophy and objectives, educational and clinical facilities, curriculum, academic preparation of instructors, student/instructor ratio, residence, and dining facilities. After travelling 57,551 miles to every province, interviewing 1,759 people, and visiting 25 participating schools (selected from 96 that volunteered), Mussallem stated in her report *Spotlight On Nursing*, 1960: "On the basis of overall quality of the total educational program, only four of the schools in the sample could have met the criteria for full accreditation had such a program been in existence." Although individual schools are not named in the report, the Calgary General Hospital School of Nursing is on record as one of these four. The source for this record has never been clear to me, but when I study the report today, with the benefit of my CGH background at the time of the study, there is no doubt in my mind that our claim is valid.

Mussallem's findings echoed those of George Weir thirty years prior, namely, that in most hospital-based training schools, the service requirements of the hospital took priority over the curriculum of the school. This order of importance gave rise to two situations: an overload of class instruction in the first year, and a lack of planning for theory and practice to run concurrently. It was also Mussallem's view that most schools provided far too few hours of instruction in the biological and physical sciences, while the social sciences were allotted a mere 6% of curriculum time. That was a lamentable allocation of time if one viewed nursing as a social science. Mussallem concluded her study with the following recommendations:

1. That a re-examination and study of the whole field of nursing education be undertaken.
2. That a school improvement program be initiated to assist schools in upgrading their educational programs.
3. That a program be established for evaluating the quality of nursing service in areas of medical practice in which students in schools of nursing received their clinical experience.
4. That a program of accreditation for schools of nursing be developed by the Canadian Nurses' Association.

Yet political pressure from powerful sources of opposition such as the Canadian Hospital Association, the Canadian Medical Association, and the *Alberta Scarlett Report* continued to impede recommendations for change. In fact, the *Scarlett Report* viewed Mussallem's study as "supplementary" only. Mussallem maintained her vision, however, with a final statement: "If, as a result of this Project, the way ahead in nursing is more clearly visible, then the efforts of the many who participated in the Project will be well rewarded."

It's interesting that the first nursing school — the "Nightingale School" in England — was developed as an independent school; its students were not under the control of St. Thomas' Hospital, nor were they part of its staff. When the system of education crossed the Atlantic, however, hospitals soon realized the potential for nursing service, and they rapidly began establishing training schools to meet their service needs. Students quickly became students in name only. By 1909 there were 70 hospital-based schools in Canada; by 1962 — the year Helen Mussallem was now engaged in another nursing study for Canada's *Royal Commission On Health Services* — the count had mushroomed to 170 such schools.

Guardians Of The Lamp

Throughout her years on this second study, Mussallem continued to buck the system, as she became ever more convinced that the focus of the established method of hospital-based nurse training was too narrow. In her report for the Royal Commission, *Nursing Education in Canada,* 1965, she argued that a nursing program should encompass social, preventative and curative aspects of nursing, in response to the *total* needs of the community. The hospital care/curative focus of the diploma program fell short of this. The goal of a new program must be to preserve the skills of the bedside nurse, while preparing the profession at large for a world in which the goal would be health. Concluding this study, Mussallem set down much more specific recommendations:

1. Programs in Canada should be revised to include a choice of one of only two categories: a two-year college diploma or a four-year baccalaureate program. The ratio should be three college students for every university student.
2. Hospital diploma schools were outdated and should be closed down. Mussallem was especially opposed to inflexible residence rules and regulations of hospital training schools. (Yay Helen! I just threw my slippers down the laundry chute!)

Two camps developed during this time: "educationists" who argued that without high educational standards, nursing would degenerate into a trade; and "service" proponents, who feared that moving nursing away from bedside care towards intellectual pursuits would, in fact, threaten the nurse's professional status. Throughout the dissension, health demands continued to grow, and immediate needs had to be addressed; the five-year university degree program and the three-year hospital diploma program were not meeting needs fast enough. The proposals in the Mussallem Report had become ever more relevant.

Ironically, in 1966, it was Ruth McClure, Director of Nursing at U of A — Gertrude Hall's old adversary — who now responded to Mussallem's recommendations by establishing a four-year integrated baccalaureate program. Her predecessor at U of A was Helen Penhale, author of the original four-year program that had been terminated. I must confess that I found it somewhat disconcerting to read in McClure's 2006 obituary: "In establishing this programme, McClure showed both vision and courage." Yet I can't deny that McClure became a dedicated champion for the nursing program's acceptance on campus alongside all other professional degree programs, or that she had the foresight to recognize the merit in allowing nursing students to mingle socially with students from other disciplines, rather than living in isolation in a hospital residence.

Dr. Helen K. Mussallem continued to serve the profession throughout her tenure as Executive Director of the Canadian Nurses' Association (1963-1981), and through a host of world-wide advisory positions. She was the first Canadian nurse to earn a PhD in nursing, and has been made a Companion of the Order of Canada. She has been aptly described as Canada's most distinguished nurse in her time and generation. She assuredly changed the course of nursing education in Canada.

The Aftermath

Following the 1965 *Mussallem Report*, a steady stream of changes in nursing education took place across the country, most rapidly in Ontario and Quebec. Five-year non-integrated university programs (BSc.N) began folding in favor of four-year integrated programs (BN), and traditional hospital-based diploma schools were faced with closure. Yet in the midst of all these transformations

— and against all national trends — the new Foothills Hospital in Calgary launched a traditional hospital-based three-year diploma program in conjunction with its opening. The Alberta Government exhibited its lingering resistance to move nursing education into the mainstream educational system when it allowed this school to open at this time.

In spite of this development, Mount Royal College bravely forged ahead with its response to Helen Mussallem's recommendations for a two-year college degree program, intended to more effectively meet the rapidly increasing staffing needs of Calgary's overflowing hospitals. In 1967, MRC initiated its program — the first of its kind outside a hospital in Calgary — under the expert directorship of Jean Mackie, whose skills in education and leadership were legendary at the Calgary General Hospital. Subsequently, Red Deer College, Lethbridge Community College and Grant MacEwan Community College, Edmonton followed suit.

The University of Calgary saw its first hint of a four-year baccalaureate program in 1968 when Dr. Shirley Good, a consultant in higher education for the Canadian Nurses' Association, visited the campus. Good firmly supported the philosophy that nursing education belonged in the mainstream system; that a nursing degree program should be based on the "social service model" of prevention, treatment and restoration. She viewed the diploma's hospital-restricted "medical model" as limiting. In 1969, Good drew up a pioneer four-year baccalaureate program at U of C, with the vision of equipping graduates with a broad range of skills needed to care for the total health of their community. Fifty students were admitted to the program in the fall of 1970. But it was not without problems.

Good was the first woman to join the group of deans and

directors heading faculties and professional schools on campus, at a time when married women with careers were criticized both within the university setting and outside it. Women were expected to choose between marriage and a career, and those who chose the latter were viewed by many as anomalies. Although women were more readily accepted in the nursing, education and social science disciplines, their positions as professors were still near the bottom of the ladder, and salaries were consistently lower than those of their male counterparts. University instructors in nursing faced two obstacles: the prejudices against *all* female professionals and the opposition to acceptance of nursing as an academic discipline within the university.

The second issue — and a significant one — was the complex problem of sharing facilities with the nearby Foothills Hospital diploma students. An affiliation contract between the two schools provided Foothills students with free access to all university facilities, yet Foothills' facilities were not equally accessible to U of C students. U of C had one meagre skills lab — a room with one bed and one mannequin — whereas the Foothills school had large well-equipped labs, which U of C could only access after hours, and for a fee. The more major problem for Good, however, was finding sites for clinical practice, since she lacked a formal hospital connection. Requests from U of C for daytime practicums at the Foothills Hospital were met with resistance from head nurses and instructors, who maintained that the baccalaureate students should adhere to the same hours of shift work as the hospital's own diploma students. This was a complicated issue to resolve.

Lastly, just a year into the developing baccalaureate program, diploma graduates in the city began petitioning the university to provide them with a post-basic degree program. University administrators agreed that the school should accommodate this request, but Good was hesitant to introduce such a program during the early stages of the school. The school initially resolved the request by offering two evening courses, although tensions over this post-basic program remained. Soon the school had more challenges: attracting its quota of 60 students for its second year and drawing needed teachers to its faculty. The decision was made that the program be evaluated. Out of three reviews, two recommended its continuation. The third reviewer expressed concern over both the operation of the program and its director. Good resigned. Overnight, fifteen faculty members and 110 students were stranded without their leader.

Fred Terentiuk, Ph.D., director of the Department of Continuing Education, stepped into the role of acting director for the next two years, skilfully guiding the school through this troubled period. Under Terentiuk's strong leadership, all the school's resources went toward developing the basic curriculum. In spite of a shaky beginning, on May 31, 1974 — the year the Calgary General Hospital School of Nursing closed its doors — 33 students took their place in history as the first graduating class of the University of Calgary's Bachelor of Nursing program. One year later, the school attained full faculty status under its first dean, Marguerite Schumacher.

In 1975, the *Alberta Task Force on Nursing Education*, while endorsing nursing education as part of the advanced educational system, recognized the need for "articulation" between the existing diploma and degree programs: a means whereby diploma students could transfer to a degree program without a delay in their advancement. The theory was sound, but conflicting loyalties complicated putting it into practice. Finally, in 1977, educators from the three groups — the college-based and hospital-based diploma programs and the university degree program — united to form a consortium that became the Alberta Nursing Educators and Administrators (ANEA). It would play an instrumental role in education policy-making.

Nursing schools — now fewer in number — increasingly faced the challenge of graduating enough nurses to meet the needs of the community, while at the same time revising programs to meet advancements in medicine. The 1970s saw nurses entering new fields, such as research; one significant study, authored by nurses, focused on the elderly — changes in mobility, crisis coping skills, rehabilitation from serious illness or surgery. Therapeutic Touch grew out of this research — energy-directed therapy that has been validated as an aid to restoring health. By the late 1970s a master's program was on the drawing boards of the U of C; the committee established to draft the program was chaired by our very own Barbara Dobbie, PhD (Class of '58) — a big sister. Its first eight students were enrolled in September 1980. The program ultimately led to the doctoral program in nursing offered today.

The 1980s brought the development of a family nursing program designed to address the needs of the entire family during the illness of one of its members. This worthwhile program was modelled after a similar one designed for medical students. The eighties also produced a refresher course for nurses who had temporarily left the workforce to raise families, paving the way for their return to active duty. Complementing this course, outreach programs were developed to meet the educational needs of nurses living in remote locations; these programs were delivered by means of interactive satellite, CD Roms, or the internet. By this time, the computer had become a fact of life, and as hospital records became computerized, nurses were confronted with learning a new, unforeseen skill.

The 1990s brought an exciting new concept in nursing education to Calgary, as administrators from three faculties recognized the advantages of a co-operative, collaborative baccalaureate program. The *Calgary Conjoint Nursing Program* was developed by the faculties of the Foothills Hospital School of Nursing, Mount Royal College and the University of Calgary over a six-year period fraught with political and institutional hurdles. In 1993, the innovative CCNP program designed to encompass three institutions teaching one program on three sites, finally launched its inaugural term with an enrolment of 301 students. Phasing in the program was tricky, and the U of C would have to deal with phasing out its original four-year baccalaureate program. Two years later, the program lost one member of the trio.

In 1995, when the Canadian Nurses' Association and its provincial affiliates agreed to close all hospital-based nursing schools, the Foothills School of Nursing closed its doors and withdrew from the CCNP. The school had operated for thirty years. The last such school in the country to close was the Victoria General Hospital School of Nursing in Halifax — also taking place in 1995 — after setting an impressive 105-year record (1890-1995) as the longest running school in Canada. These closures truly marked the end of an era.

The CCNP continued on with its two remaining faculties at the helm until 2000, when Mount Royal College decided to withdraw on the grounds that "we have been consistent in insisting that this agreement reflect a meaningful partnership rather than a relationship between a lead and supporting institution." It was MRC's view that "the university's insistence upon retaining ultimate control over such fundamental matters as curriculum, records, budget and decision-making has undermined the principles that led to forming the conjoint program in the first place." The partnership failed, but the program passed the test of graduating excellent students who were well received by the medical community.

In 2007, MRC proudly launched a Bachelor of Nursing program — its first independent baccalaureate program. The U of C offers a host of advanced programs in addition to its basic baccalaureate program. These include a Bachelor of Nursing Accelerated Track (BNAT) and a Nurse Practitioner program, both of which run in conjunction with its masters and doctoral programs. The expanded role of the Nurse Practitioner has been an invaluable asset to the community in meeting the shortage of physicians. The university maintains a wide range of cooperative partnerships: locally, with the Calgary Health Region and Mount Royal College; provincially, with Medicine Hat College; nationally, with the Centennial College in Toronto and Dalhousie University in Halifax; and internationally, with Kagaw Medical University in Japan and the University of Tampere in Finland. In 2008, the U of C School of Nursing launched a collaborative program in Doha, Qatar, affirming once more a desire to be a partner in global health care. Currently, Alberta has eleven approved university and college programs offering entry level baccalaureate nursing education, most with diploma exit available. Most maintain collaboration with one or more sister schools.

Gertrude Hall would be astounded at the changes in bedside nursing in today's world of short hospital stays and high intensity patient care. But I picture her smiling with satisfaction on learning that her crusade for change has been realized. I have great faith that Alberta's nursing schools are producing a spectacular crop of highly skilled and dedicated women and men solidly armed to carry us into the future.

Today's nurses have achieved the elevated status that was Gertrude Hall's dream. But can they fashion a bedside waste bag out of a newspaper? Carry a bedpan with any degree of finesse? Take a temperature with a *real* thermometer? And I suspect Gertrude would *not* be smiling over one critical experience the student nurse

in today's education system is denied: life in residence — restricted
hours, ridiculous rules, mandatory slippers, and up and down the
halls, the birth of a sisterhood that lasts a lifetime.

End of the Road for the Calgary General Hospital

The first of the changes to come took place in 1988 with the
opening of the Peter Lougheed Centre under the umbrella of the
Calgary General Hospital. The physical building we had always
known as the Calgary General Hospital was forthwith assigned a
new name: Bow Valley Centre. Under the direction of one board,
the Calgary General Hospital now operated as one hospital on two
sites with a combined total of 1,000 beds. It considered itself a
leading teaching and referral centre for southern Alberta. Plans to
entirely rejuvenate the physical facilities of the Bow Valley Centre
were underway.

Operating in tandem, both medical centres offered complete
clinical services, with the exception of select disciplines that were
consolidated under one roof. The Bow Valley Centre, for example,
was the sole provider for diabetes care; intensive care; psychiatry;
convalescence and rehabilitation; and palliative care. The Peter
Lougheed Centre maintained facilities for pediatrics; obstetrics
and gynecology; and eye, ear, nose and throat. The Calgary General
eagerly looked forward to a future in keeping with its past — a caring
approach and a commitment to excellence. Then on December 14,
1992, Ralph Klein was sworn in as Alberta's twelfth premier.

In 1993, Klein announced a four-year plan to balance the budget
by eliminating the government's $3.4 billion deficit. A new budget
composed of massive cuts was developed to stem soaring costs.
Many education and social programs were greatly reduced, and
health care — a prime target — was turned on its head. In 1994,

hospital boards disbanded, as health authorities were formed to assume responsibility for the planning and delivering of health services: the Calgary Regional Health Authority for Calgary and Southern Alberta and the Capital Health Authority for Edmonton and Northern Alberta. Under these un-elected health authorities, hospitals were closed province wide, reducing our hospital count from 125 to 103. The bed count dropped from 4.3 per thousand residents to 2.4 per thousand. Nurses' hours were reduced or nurses were replaced by less qualified auxiliary staff at lower wages.

Calgary's three historic inner city hospitals — the Holy Cross, the Grace and the Calgary General — were selected for closure, and the General was targeted for demolition. It would mean a loss of hundreds of beds at a time when the city's population was skyrocketing. "There's no question this is a different era for public health care policy," said Richard Plain, a University of Alberta health economist. "The delivery of health care has changed and we don't need as many hospital beds as we once did," he added. His statement was based on the premise that advances in technology were reducing patients' recovery times, and in more and more instances, procedures once requiring a week's hospital stay were now being managed by outpatient services, which eliminated the need for beds entirely.

The Holy Cross and the Grace Hospitals closed in 1996, although in the end, each continue to extend medical services to the community. The Holy Cross Centre houses day facilities for a wide variety of diagnostic and treatment specialties, from breast screening, cardiovascular evaluation and eye surgery to advanced spinal care and chronic pain. The Grace Hospital was purchased by a group of private investors — HRG, Health Resource Group. The group's Health Resource Centre is a first class 37-bed facility dedicated to leadership in expedited care. It provides surgical —

most notably, joint replacement — and diagnostic procedures, as well as assessment and inpatient medical and rehabilitation services. The Calgary General — the last surviving downtown hospital — would not be so fortunate. It would not live to serve again.

In 1995, a head-to-head battle began between two dissenting parties over the General's destiny. A provincial government bent on wiping the slate of an ageing facility, in order to streamline its new health care scheme, was pitted against a legion of Calgary citizens who loved their city and the pioneer hospital that was an integral part of it — a safe place that had faithfully and compassionately served them, and their families, for generations. Dale Eisler, in his *Maclean's* article of April 28, 1997, aptly described the General as "a doting grandmother presiding over the city." In order to justify its position on demolishing her, however, a single-minded health authority viewed her as an old, dysfunctional, money-gobbling behemoth. To her grandchildren, such a cold-hearted dismissal was unthinkable; she had earned a place of honor in her city, and they intended to put up a fight. In a community hall below the General, a group of about forty active citizens gathered. In this humble setting they organized an official *Keep the General* committee, and launched their fight.

Keep the General argued that the Calgary Regional Health Authority, in eliminating costs to restore and continue operating the General from its health care budget, was failing to adequately address the resulting increased costs that the other hospitals would incur in replacement services. Additionally, emergency and urgent care doctors warned of the possible dire consequences of a city the size of Calgary safely providing urgent care for its population without a downtown hospital — a circumstance unheard of in the entire country. *Keep the General* argued that the General was the most accessible hospital in the city from any direction; its renowned, attainable trauma centre had saved countless lives. But just as importantly, the CHRA was failing to regard the emotional health and well-being of the thousands of Calgarians who had known the comforting embrace of the General through births, deaths and illnesses throughout their entire lives. The facility that had watched over them in the past, would, they trusted, stand vigil for their future.

I remember gasping when I read a quote in a newspaper clip one day from someone reluctantly conceding to the hospital's demise; "Perhaps the old girl has just come of age," the author lamented. The *old girl* was 44 years old; I was 60 and thinking I was still pretty spry! It must be that hospitals have their own formula for ageing, I decided, sort of the way dogs do. Maybe in hospital years the old girl was over the hill... except that she was only thirteen years older than the Foothills Hospital. Actually, two of her main buildings were younger than the Foothills. But no argument was going to break the will of a Conservative premier determined to achieve his agenda, regardless of the ramifications. I have often wondered if Ralph Klein ever had misgivings at any point, but was unwilling to admit an error in judgement and reverse his course.

Many fought passionately to save the General. Medical staff, such as Dr. Tom Rich and Dr. Rob Abernethy, and the Chairwoman of the Board, Mairi Matheson, indicated a willingness to accept a scaled-down version of the General as a viable medical centre offering urgent care. Thousands of Calgarians implored their government to save their beloved institution. *Keep the General* committee members made concerted efforts. Among these members was a resolute Dr. Harold Swanson, staunch Conservative and long-time Calgary General radiologist, who faced off against Premier Klein politically, first attempting to unseat him for the Tory nomination, and failing that, challenging his riding on the Liberal ticket. Joe Ceci, Bob Hawkesworth and John Schmal, city aldermen, went to war to heed the cries of their constituents and answer the call of their own convictions. Gordon Christie, John Currie and Jim Webster, dedicated community volunteers, fought for their beloved hospital until the last breath. In spite of all these efforts, the battle to save the General was lost. With breaking hearts, we were compelled to release Grandma to the gods.

The sheer magnitude of demobilizing a hospital of this size is beyond my imagining. Those who were involved in the intricacies of transferring patients and equipment piecemeal to specified receiving facilities, spread throughout the city, have my undying admiration. Such a feat had never been undertaken by a hospital of this size in North America. Needless to say, the first priority in the choreography was the safety of the patients. The Calgary General's dedicated staff teams would accept no less than their unparalleled care through the transition, as they painstakingly worked out their strategy. The most pressing concerns were for the emergency and intensive care units transferring to the Peter Lougheed Centre. The dicey timing of closing the General's emergency, and getting it up and running in its merged form with the urgent care unit of the PLC, was hair-raising. The seven days it took to get the intensive care unit operational in its new home was another period of high anxiety for all involved. Dismantling the CT scan took five hours; transferring the MRI system with hoists and cranes took five days.

Long-term rehabilitation patients were uprooted from the security of their daily routines — programs that were steadily inching them toward renewed health. Nurses were apprehensive, fatigued, and overwhelmingly sad. Some were angry. Many had worked together as teams to develop finely-tuned programs that ran with precision, a mark of their trust in one another. They were family. Suddenly, their worlds were ripped apart; they were sent packing across town to make a new life in uncharted territory. A grieving emergency department held a private wake. This tightly-knit group of nurses considered the 50,000 people they tended to a year — including a large population of street people suffering mental illnesses — to be part of their family. They wept openly as the presiding chaplain, Brown Milne, attempted to console them with the assurance, "There will be life after death."

Calgarians awake to a clear blue sky on October 4, 1998 — sunny Alberta living up to its name. It is 4°C, but feels colder. A chilling wind sweeps across the city, heralding the coming of winter. The detonation is scheduled for 9:00 a.m., and thousands of spectators are drawn to areas surrounding the hospital to witness the spectacle. From above, on the Colgrove Avenue embankment and in Tom Campbell Park, are a sea of men, women, children, pets, lawn chairs, blankets and binoculars. Down below, police battle the masses creating a log jam along Memorial Drive. Further throngs find a vantage point atop Scotia Centre, the Petro Canada building, the Calgary Tower. Across the country, hundreds of thousands are glued to their television screens awaiting the countdown. Thousands more can't bear to watch; they stop their day to stand in reverent silence at the appointed hour. 10... 9... 8...

The silence is broken by the thunder of dynamite, the ground trembles, and the hospital tumbles in on itself. In 23 seconds, the Calgary General Hospital — the city's grand old lady — is reduced to rubble. Then she disappears entirely, engulfed in a cloud of dust. Tears flow as a city's skyline is altered forever. Calgary Herald reporters (October 5, 1998) capture comments from devotees especially close to the morning's catastrophe:

Mairi Matheson, the hospital board's last chairwoman, moans,

"It feels so much like a funeral. I didn't really believe this was ever going to happen… my heart is breaking."

"I'm grieving. I really am," says Dr. William Grisdale, long-time Calgary General physician, who was born at the General, as were his mother and his children. "I've lost part of my life, part of my family."

Jody Butler, who grew up across the street from the General, defies evacuation orders by creeping into the bell tower of St. Matthew's Lutheran Church with fellow mourners, aiming to be as near as possible to their cherished hospital. It was as though they wanted to reach across and hold her hand as she took her last breath. "This is like watching a loved one die," Jody whispers.

The Aftermath

October 4, 2003. The fifth anniversary of the General's demolition resurrects old memories and stirs up harbored resentments. The city's population has been growing at a rate of close to 20,000 people a year; its health care system is stressed to the limit. Kevin Taft, provincial Liberal health critic, has harsh words for the custodians of our well-being. "Destroying the Calgary General was maybe the worst decision the Calgary Health Region has ever made," he said. "To demolish a major hospital in the fastest-growing city in Canada is short-sighted beyond description." (Calgary Herald, Sunday October 5, 2003.) The CRHA continues to defend its decision, claiming it saved the system $180 million — the cost that would have been borne in restoring the General — a figure highly disputed by protesters. At the time of the demolition in 1998, the Region indicated the city would need a new hospital by 2003. The prediction was well-founded, but the Region has not been forthcoming. Plans are finally in the works for the still-deserted Calgary General land — land that had been transferred to the City of Calgary on the condition that the city provide the province with 12.5 acres for a new hospital in southeast Calgary.

Soon after the 2003 anniversary date, I learn that the city has sold eight parcels of this hospital land to developers, and plans are conceived for a multifamily residential and mixed-use development. "The Bridges" — forecast to house 2,000 to 2,500 residents — is to be a pedestrian-friendly urban village that "respects, enhances and takes cues from the surrounding neighborhood." It's planning concepts will be guided by the City of Calgary's previously formulated Bow Valley Centre Concept Plan that included input from members of a Public Advisory Committee and residents of the surrounding Bridgeland community. Integral to the Bridges — intended to develop in three phases over a nine-year period — is a base of sustainability and energy-efficiency. One of the most significant characteristics of its blueprint is the preservation of almost one third of the land for open space.

The following spring, further word on this development reaches the press, and I'm spurred across town to inspect the state of my old stomping ground. I find little in the way of construction, except a bizarre-looking "wall to nowhere" parked in the middle of a desolate open space. As I draw closer, the letters "CALGARY GENERAL HOSPITAL 1910 - 1998" come into focus across the top of the wall. Then I spot the rows of unmistakable brick embedded in its face, and realize that I am standing on the actual site of my old hospital. Yet I feel no gratitude for this commemorative wall — this token chunk of charity jutting from a patch of bleak, barren land. A bone-chilling wind is whirling around the wall, and I shiver uncontrollably. The wall does not cut the wind. It brings me no warmth.

On a hot sunny day in August, 2008, I visit the site again, this time with a CGH sister. Jean and I stroll the streets of the fully completed Phase I of The Bridges; the infrastructure for Phase II on lands adjoining Memorial Drive and the LRT in the distance below, is complete, but construction of the buildings is still not underway. We note that the laundry — the last remnant of the hospital — has disappeared, and the land has been stripped in preparation for Phase III — the final phase — to be situated on its site . It's evident that the original nine-year timetable for completion of The Bridges, will extend to ten years or more.

We sit for a bit on a promenade bench that overlooks Murdoch Park — a huge expanse of lush green, encompassing soccer fields and a large community hall — and as we collect our bearings, we begin to see the "footprint" of our hospital within this green space. Memories of our student days within the park's perimeter come flooding back. Young trees are taking root along the promenade that runs the length of the new-sprung condos above the park, and the commemorative wall, now embraced by the park's greenery, has taken on a new, inviting look. From the wall's east side, downtown office towers can be seen poking their heads over top, as if to keep a watchful eye on things. I later learn that the wall marks the site where a wall of the hospital once stood. I also learn that the developers intend to prohibit any construction of housing units within the borders of the park.

...the commemorative wall has taken on a new, inviting look.

Photo: courtesy Jean McLennan

Murdoch Park and the Calgary General Commemorative Wall will forever hold a place of honor in the heart of The Bridges community. Jean and I wrap up the afternoon with sandwiches, tea and conversation at a patio cafe on "General Avenue." We decide all is well in our new world.

...new-sprung condos above Murdoch Park...

October 4, 2008. On the tenth anniversary of the General's demolition, a small group of mourners gather at the commemorative wall to remember and honor their departed hospital. Among them is John Schmal, the last vice-chair on the General Hospital's board and a vigorous crusader to save his hospital. Still suffering intense sorrow over the loss, he is not reluctant to criticize city council, and others, for not fighting harder to save her. "We all know what happened here was the very worst blunder ever made by a health care board," he tells a *Calgary Herald* reporter (Sunday, October 5, 2008). Rebecca Aizenman, a fellow crusader, also in attendance, has stronger words, quoted in the same article: "This is the '9/11' of health care," she said. "We haven't recovered from it. The meltdown is still felt today."

Photo: courtesy Jean McLennan

I am grateful for the Aizenmans and the Schmals of this city, who cared to the core for our hospital, and fought to the end to save her. They will be troubled with fellow citizens, who either didn't care or were too complacent to join the fight. Their bitterness is understandable, and the current situation of long wait lists, overflowing emergency departments, and hospital corridors that look like gurney parkades, is raising the ire of all Calgarians. Long awaited construction of the South Health Campus began in August, 2007, its price tag having doubled since the original estimate of $550 million two years prior. By 2008, the price tag has reached $1.25 billion, and beds for obstetrics and mental health are sacrificed to accommodate the cost increase. The first phase — now scaled back — is targeted to open in 2011, and the entire hospital, by 2017. I wonder what Calgary's population will be by that time. Meanwhile, my prescription for maintaining my mental and emotional health is a nostalgic stroll through Murdoch Park with a good friend, and a cuppa on the General Avenue plaza.

General Avenue — we decide all is well in our new world.

Chapter 7

– GUARDIANS OF THE LAMP –

Birth of a Sisterhood

It began on a cold December day with a circle of friends and their mentor sharing ideas for the future over coffee and cake. The room radiated with the warmth of this particular circle of friends — sisters, actually — born from a shared past as student nurses at the Calgary General Hospital. Their mentor was Sara MacDonald, their adored Superintendent of Nurses, who had a mission for calling the group together. Sara, a graduate of the Massachusetts General Hospital, knew the benefits of an alumnae association, and urged these young women to give serious consideration to forming their own. As she pointed out the unifying potential of a formal organization, as well as the professional advantages, heads were already nodding in agreement.

The group put out the word the next day, and weren't surprised to discover that it travelled from sister to sister like lightening, just as it had when they were students. On January 8, 1936 some 90 graduates of the school gathered in "A" Block — the existing residence at the time — and shared their vision for an alumnae association. Then, they set to work drawing up a constitution and by laws, and before the close of day, the Alumnae Association of the Calgary General Hospital School of Nursing was official.

The school had graduated 614 students by that date, and everyone contacted had responded with enthusiasm; a longing for news of classmates was expressed everywhere. Within a year, they had rallied a paid-up membership of 290. Elizabeth Straker (Shirley '25), the association's first president, famously described it as a "lusty infant." Within three years, members in good standing jumped to 398, and local meetings regularly averaged over 100 eager participants. But, of course, they paid the price of success when "A" Block could no longer accommodate them.

On January 8, 1936 some 90 graduates of the school gathered in "A" Block...

They first moved to the "Knights of Columbus" room under the Grand Theatre, although minutes of the time suggest there was a distinct drawback to these quarters — one that almost put the kibosh on the otherwise happy relationship between the knights and the nurses. Apparently, the knights were an unsanitary lot when it came to their kitchen, and the alumnae threatened to take their business elsewhere if they did not clean it up. I am comforted to know that these enterprising women of the thirties rejected the assumption that kitchen duty was part of their contract. In any event, meetings thrived, whether in the Knights' dungeon, in members' private homes or in space donated by doctors at the Calgary Associate Clinic, and the CGH Alumnae Association continued to grow. Scrounging for a venue became a fact of life, but it would not deter this unshakeable group of women. However, as numbers grew, so did the challenge of maintaining contact with everyone.

To address this issue, the alumnae developed an elaborate communication system: they divided the city into zones, with each zone assigned a captain. The captain was responsible for conveying information to and from the alumnae with everyone in her zone, and for maintaining an up-to-date address list. When the system was first developed in 1940, there were six zones; by 1961 there were fifty. By that time, alumnae association "satellites" had also cropped up in Lethbridge, Edmonton and Vancouver.

Then graduating classes grew larger... and larger, and our numbers grew exponentially. As well, there was an increased prevalence of sisters living far from our borders. We now counted on the networking of individual classes to keep records current. To this date, with class and individual input, our alumnae association maintains a master record of every graduate of the Calgary General Hospital. Death dates of those we have lost are also recorded. Regrettably, we have a handful of sisters whose whereabouts we have never been able to trace — the Class of '59 has one — but like mothers who have lost a child, we never stop looking, and we never give up hope that we'll find them.

Following the school's closure in 1974, our numbers began to dwindle; there is no new blood to replace the passing of the guard. Living with this reality, however, has increased our comradeship many fold; we look after one another as never before. A biannual bulletin travels the globe in the spring and the fall to keep everyone apprised of our news, and for those who do not receive it — or do not retain its data — another opportunity awaits them at our annual banquet in May when all the news — and more — is repeated at least one more time. Our network system has become impressively streamlined into one zone — located in cyberspace. It receives an upgrade each time another brave soul ventures online. When there's a death in the family, word reaches everyone with a keystroke, and we all mourn.

A Benevolent Society

Although establishment of the alumnae association was rooted in the desire of CGH graduates to maintain a connection with one another, they soon recognized that a strong membership such as theirs could serve the needs of their hospital, and in turn, their community. They were quick to spot where they could best serve, and wasted no time getting down to business. Their first fundraising project was extremely ambitious.

In 1939, the alumnae organized its first Ice Carnival, recruiting figure skating stars from Edmonton, Saskatoon, Banff and our own Glencoe Club in Calgary. It was a monumental task to organize the affair and promote ticket sales, but the end result surpassed all expectations; the performance on Calgary's first artificial ice brought an atmosphere of professionalism to the sparkling new Victoria Arena. It was a huge financial success. For seven years that included the war years, this annual backbreaking event, headed by Gertrude O'Keefe (Barrett '24), was a major fundraiser for the association, often clearing over $2,000.00 — a serious amount in the 1940s.

Drawing up a list of beneficiaries for these funds now rose to the top of the agenda at alumnae association meetings. The needs at home were endless, and the alumnae regularly came to the rescue with donations of furnishings and medical equipment for the hospital. Soon, however, the needs created by a world war overshadowed those at home and much of their attention turned to the war effort. Their benevolence was extended to all manner of relief funds: the Red Cross, Russian Relief, Chinese Relief, London's Lord Mayor's Fund, Prisoner of War Fund, Christmas Cheer For British Children. And of course, they gave generously to the Overseas Nurses' Fund, while additionally mailing care packages to their own CGH sisters serving on the front. The women met regularly to pack these parcels, and they always slipped snippets of news inside, and words of encouragement from home. The names of those who served are inscribed on the Honor Roll found in our alumnae Book of Memory. We are proud of these brave sisters.

The personal touch of the alumnae frequently travelled beyond their own sisters during the war; they regularly organized work bees to sew, write letters and pack parcels of food and clothing for the servicemen overseas. And whenever possible, they stretched their funds to add an item they knew would win the hearts of their Canadian soldiers: a pack of cigarettes. Today we know more about the effect of cigarettes on hearts, but the well-intentioned gift no doubt had medicinal value under the circumstances. One project that perhaps carried more meaning than any, was the adoption, through Foster Parents' Plan, of a Greek refugee child named Anastasia. Nurses from three particular classes — '48, '51 and '53 — made Anastasia their post-war mission, meeting regularly to mend used clothing, collect what they could in the way of food and household essentials, and mail them off with personal greetings to Anastasia's family.

Throughout the long period of sacrifice for the war effort, one indulgence comically recurs in the minutes of meetings — the issue of refreshments for the next meeting. Refreshments were clearly of paramount importance — what to serve, how much to bring, whose responsibility. They justified their accommodation with the certainty that nurses need fuel to function. Yet daily they were bombarded with evidence of food shortages the world over, until finally one day, when the last crumb of Emily's chocolate cake had disappeared, they made a spontaneous decision: they would give up refreshments — cold turkey. (Or rather, no cold turkey.) Whether this supreme sacrifice for the war effort was a virtuous act or whether it was motivated by guilt, they nevertheless held true to their commitment, and not a morsel of food accompanied anyone to the next meeting. It posed only one problem: attendance plunged. Minutes from a subsequent meeting revealed, "we went back to eating."

A post-war alumnae association decided the time had come to terminate the annual encumbering ice carnival, and so, armed with the return of sustenance, members directed their energies toward raising funds by other means: art exhibits, raffles, rummage sales, teas and even a moccasin dance. And they weren't averse to approaching local businesses for assistance with topping up the coffers. Now, too, their attention turned back to the home front and the never-ending list of items needed by the hospital, the school and the nurses' residence. They were also great supporters of education, donating on a regular basis to the In-service Fund for supplementary tuition for graduates.

By the late forties, the alumnae had attained a prominent, respected status city-wide; the Hospital Board and the business community frequently sought their advice and support. They capitalized on this solid standing by successfully going to bat for themselves in three areas:

1. They urged their Hospital Board to become pro-active in raising the General Hospital's rating as assessed by the American College of Physicians and Surgeons. At that time, it had a second-class rating, which graduates viewed as a disadvantage when applying for positions elsewhere.
2. They fought for hospitalization benefits for themselves, gaining a 40% reduction for medical and room charges, plus a hospital scheme to cover maternity costs.
3. They fought for better working condition for students. (Bless them!)

The 1950s dawned a new era — the age of Gertrude Hall, Dr. L. O. Bradley and a new hospital. Hall and Bradley arrived in the fall of 1952 to a hospital under construction. They considered the alumnae association an active partner in the mammoth project, and frequented association meetings to confer with members on particulars as it progressed. Members were taken on group tours during the construction period, and were invited to contribute their ideas for the design and operation of the new facility. It was an exciting time.

Gertrude Hall, a plainspoken woman who was used to being in command, recognized at the outset that the Calgary General Alumnae Association was a force to reckon with. These women of stature were not reluctant to speak their minds in opposition to the new director. The association was rooted in a history of intimacy with the hospital it had faithfully served, and members were not receptive to the idea that the new kid on the block could propose overnight changes to their long-time methods of operation. As a result, the two forces were frequently at loggerheads, although it is more than likely that Gertrude Hall held great respect for women whose motivation and strength rivalled her own.

The 1950s was also the advent of arguably the alumnae association's biggest fundraiser — the November Mitten Tea. It's reputation became legion throughout the city. In the early years, the tea was held at Central United Church, but my memory of it begins with my student years when it was held in our sunken lounge. When I see shoppers today stampeding *Best Buy* for the latest *X-Box* game hitting the shelves, I'm reminded of the flood of women pressing up against the south doors of the residence awaiting their opening for the Mitten Tea.

Tea and fancies were served at beautifully appointed tables, and honored hospital staff members were invited to pour. Around the perimeter of the lounge, craft tables were set up to display the varied handiwork of alumnae members, but the main feature of the event was the array of hand knit mittens in every size and shade — a sea of dazzling colors spreading from table to table. In the lead-up to the big day, the knitting needles of alumnae clicked for months in homes all over town and for miles around. I remember my first contribution as a student. It was my first stab at knitting, and those mitts took me forever to make. They were royal blue and had disproportionately large thumbs that stuck straight up. I kept my eye on them as each customer passed by them, then danced for joy when some dear soul picked them up. I didn't notice whether she had big thumbs. I knew I had tired thumbs.

In 1955, the alumnae association undertook its most ambitious project to date. The new residence was under construction, and the dream was to build a non-denominational chapel within its walls as a memorial to all who graduated from the Calgary General Hospital. The shared vision of the alumnae was to establish, furnish and maintain a chapel to call their own. They approached the City of Calgary for permission, and it was granted right away.

Under the leadership of their president, Mary MacDonald (Cumberland '20), the alumnae began the Herculean task of contacting every last graduate — now numbering 1,490 — to allow each one an opportunity to contribute to the cause. The response from sisters was overwhelming, and the little chapel united the alumnae as never before. Hearts were especially touched when a cheque for $1,000.00 arrived for the Chapel Fund from Marion Moodie, the General's first graduate fifty-seven years prior. In some instances, classes pooled their resources to sponsor a specific item such as a baptismal font or a pew in memory of a deceased sister.

The chapel was formally dedicated by the Rt. Reverend C.R. Calvert, Bishop of Calgary, on May 12, 1956 — a date that coincidentally marked the twentieth anniversary of the alumnae's inception. It was a banner day for the alumnae association; the chapel would be a source of great pride forever after. Gertrude Hall, a strong Christian, especially loved the chapel, and when alumnae weren't looking, she sort of claimed it as hers. I remember her making the chapel the first stop when escorting civic dignitaries on tours of the new residence. I can still see her smiling broadly as she waltzed her guests down the corridor and waved them into *her* private little heaven.

The chapel was fully furnished with pews, altar and organ, but two items capturing our hearts for all time would come later: the Book of Memory, to record the names of all graduates and honorees, and the stained glass window, designed by Eleanor Tregillus (Robertson '37) and her husband, Dick. Eleanor understood the challenge she and her window committee faced as they put their heads together to conceive a design. The chapel was built as a memorial to the past, and they wanted the window to reflect this fact. Yet it would be installed in a new chapel, in a modern residence, as a place of worship for young students looking to the future. The committee members were certain of one thing: they would not find a template in a studio anywhere that would fulfil their vision. And so, they set about designing the window themselves, and with deep thought, they wove all the elements that tell our story into a breathtaking work of art:

1. The school pin, a red cross on a circular backing, unchanged since its beginning.
2. The symbolic nurse's lamp representing "service never faltering; faith never failing."
3. The Caduceus — a winged staff entwined by two serpents, the medical symbol of healing.
4. The biblical quotation, "Jesus went about healing all manner of sickness," taken from Matthew IV, verse 23.

5. A background of prairie flowers and grains; treed foothills; majestic mountains and sunny skies, substituting the traditional biblical setting with symbols of our own province.
6. The principal figures:
    i a baby, signifying how God first came to us on earth.
    ii a nurse, committing herself to the Golden Rule in caring for others.
    iii the Christus, signifying the nurse's acceptance that life and death ultimately lie in the hands of a higher power.

The window and the Book of Memory were dedicated in May 1957, one year after the opening of the residence and the chapel. The same month, the long-standing annual alumnae banquet was held in the residence auditorium for the first time, so the window was the center of attention. Four hundred nineteen attendees squeezed up and down the aisle of the chapel that night to marvel together at their spectacular gift.

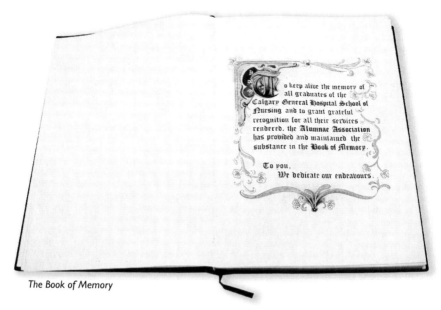

The Book of Memory

After the school's closure, the proximity of the residence to the hospital made it an ideal location for reassignment: main floor residence rooms were adopted by medical specialists for office space, while rooms on the upper floors were utilized as sleeping quarters for staff, outpatients or out-of-town visitors to the hospital. But no one came to morning chapel.

Once again, the alumnae rallied forces and the association put in a bid to the hospital

*Stained glass window,
now in the Peter Lougheed Center.*

board for a place where the chapel could be given second life. In 1977, it was moved to the main corridor of the hospital, where staff and visitors were grateful for the solace and solitude they could find in its warm embrace. The alumnae continued to love and care for the chapel in its new setting; minutes from a 1993 meeting reveal proud alumnae examining the pleasing new carpet and pew covers they had provided. Then rumblings of desertion were heard once again. The Alumnae Memorial Chapel would not survive doomsday.

In advance of the demise of Bow Valley Centre, furnishings from the chapel made their way to local community churches. The items closest to our hearts were welcomed in the existing chapel at the Peter Lougheed Centre: plaques removed from original furnishings, the memorial windows and the treasured Book of Memory, which our archivist, Flora McInnes (McNeill '46), watches over with passionate devotion. Flora protects our Book of Memory as she would her Family Bible. The book is locked in a glassed case that only Flora and the hospital chaplain can access. Flora tells me that each time she visits, the book is opened to a new page, providing evidence of the chaplain at work. I'm comforted to know that my name will rise to a place of prominence every now and then.

On an inner wall of the chapel, you will find a plaque indicating its original designation, the Leslie Wilson Roberts Chapel. It is so named in honor of a much admired chairman of the Calgary General Hospital Board who served from 1974 to 1982. Above its outer doors you will find its modern-day designation — "Sacred Space" — to welcome followers of every faith. I can't help thinking that the space would be more sacred without unsightly hospital notices taped to the chapel's entrance doors.

Sacred Space of
the Peter Lougheed Centre.

The stained glass window that Eleanor Tregillus so lovingly designed for her sisters, and for her God, is discreetly located in a dimly lit corner of the chapel, where it places no demand for attention from those of non-Christian faiths. When I sit quietly beside that window, I find peace.

The alumnae association currently boasts a paid-up membership of 730 women the world over, anxious to maintain ties with their alma mater. Locally, the old guard has faithfully carried the ball for the operation of the association, by volunteering in positions as officers and committee heads for years. More recently, the Class of '62 has stepped up to the plate, taking on some of the leadership roles. Members gather about four times a year to share news of sisters and plan for the year's upcoming events. Rigorous fund-raising projects have become a thing of the past, but a philanthropic spirit lives on. In conjunction with the University of Calgary, the alumnae association funds a $2,500.00 bursary for a second-year nursing student, with preferential treatment awarded to a child or grandchild of a CGH graduate. In the absence of such a candidate, criteria of need are assessed. Donations to the fund maintaining the bursary are generous, and are frequently sent by sisters in memory of classmates they have lost.

Recently, the alumnae supplied the "sacred space" at the PLC with an intriguing addition: a labyrinth carpet, as desired by those who experience a spiritual presence walking its paths. Every Wednesday afternoon, it is rolled out on the floor, and followers find release with each step circling the labyrinth. The carpet is one more small connection we have to a place that originated through the spirit of alumnae members.

Stored Treasures

In addition to the names and dates engraved in our Book of Memory, and the current events recorded in our biannual newsletters, long-standing remembrances are preserved for posterity in archives stored under lock and key at the Peter Lougheed Centre. The keeper of the key is Flora McInnes, our chief archivist, who guards them with her life.

Entering the west doors of the PLC, you will find a corridor of memorabilia — a timeline of our history — stretching down the north wall. Along the south wall are intermittent display cases containing all manner of collectables, ranging from medical instruments to a parade of school uniforms. The first person to greet you is Marion Moodie, a life-sized mannequin of our first graduate, originally donated by the Museum Department of the Calgary Brewing and Malting Company. She made her debut in 1967 in the Centennial Display housed in the old reading room of the residence. The Centennial Display was a project launched by Jean McIntyre (Moon '31), an active member of the alumnae association who became one of its early archivists. Dr. Maryon Robertson (Class of '48) took up the cause for many years, ambitiously collecting enough stuff to fill an entire museum. That, however, was an unattainable dream.

The display cases in the PLC are a treasure for sure, but stashed in hiding are the treasures that personally touch me the most — a staggering fifteen volumes of photos, personal letters, graduation programs, and news clips dating back to the 1920s. Contributions to the collection have clearly been offered willy-nilly, occasionally creating an accumulation of the same news clip on multiple pages of one volume, or in some instances, repeated in multiple volumes. But never mind — you can't read a story you love too many times. Sometimes a class began a volume in memory of a sister who died; other times, a milestone anniversary drew collectibles for a volume. One class has individual documents for each classmate, reading like résumés recording both careers and personal lives. A few volumes, especially the early ones, contain photos and news clips that begin with a class's graduation, and progress through each life in slow motion: careers, weddings, children and grandchildren, with class reunion photos dotted in-between. I felt so sad when the inevitable obituaries began cropping up. I laughed when I read a long-suffering husband's complaint, "Marry a nurse and you marry the whole damn alumnae."

News clips are especially fun and informative. Who knew that the actress Valerie Harper of "Rhoda" fame was the daughter of a CGH grad — Iva Harper (McConnell '35)? Or that our beloved Mrs. "O," Gertrude O'Keefe, who headed up those ice carnivals beginning in 1939, volunteered twenty-three years of service to the Blood Donor Clinic at Red Cross House, consistently logging more hours than the paid staff? Her retirement in 1970 commanded much press, and so it should have. And who remembers Hidy and Howdy, the Olympic Mascots, making a guest appearance at our 1987 Homecoming Banquet? As I scanned the pages of each volume, sprinkled with news of adventures and achievements, I was constantly aware of those who valued their family of sisters enough to tuck each item into this bounty of remembrances for all time. An ongoing volume lies in the caring hands of our ever watchful Flora McInnes, who adds each noteworthy treasure that comes her way.

Merrymaking in May

In spite of the alumnae association's long list of diversions down through the years — ice carnivals, knitting bees, wartime parcels, a peacetime chapel — members never lost sight of their original objective: the companionship and support of fellow sisters. Welcoming each new graduating class to the fold topped the list of priorities from the dawning of the association, when the first banquet was organized to celebrate the occasion. It would become the association's premier event of the year forever after.

The first alumnae banquet was held on May 8, 1936 — an ambitious undertaking for an association still in its infancy. Graduation exercises for 32 graduates from the Class of '36 had previously taken place at Central United Church. Afterward, they had filed across the street in their stiff, sparkling whites for a reception on the fifth-floor auditorium of the Hudson Bay Company. Now they would be fêted by their senior sisters at a banquet in the Alhambra Room on the fourth flour of the department store down the street — the T. Eaton Company. That banquet, marked by sisters from all classes breaking bread together, was the foundation for the alumnae celebration that has taken place every May since that date. The tradition of big and little sisters was initiated at the 1946 banquet. Witnessing the spirit and the scope of the alumnae in the fifties, Gertrude Hall announced her strong belief that the Calgary General Hospital Nurses' Alumnae Association was the largest and strongest in Canada. When Gertrude Hall spoke, we listened.

Elizabeth Straker, in her capacity as the first president, spoke to the gathering, of loneliness graduates feel on leaving their hospital and their classmates to strike out on their own. "For some, the feeling can be overwhelming," she acknowledged. "For you, the Class of 1936, we trust that the alumnae may mean a closing up of broken links... that you may find the tie to sustain your interest and your unity with your school." After pointing out the reciprocal benefits of those in attendance — the fresh enthusiasm of the new graduates and the wise experience of their senior counterparts — she concluded with the affirmation, "Once a nurse, always a nurse."

After the banquet's debut at Eaton's, it moved to the Renfrew Club for three years, before settling into the Palliser Hotel for the next sixteen. When the new residence opened, however, we had a place in our very own home to hold the banquet. For four years, which included my graduating year, Beaver Catering performed miracles by delivering to the residence the exact amount of food needed to serve all attending. They used the organizer's best estimate of numbers expected as their guide. In the absence of pre-sold tickets, the caterers and organizers always flew by the seat of their pants, yet, as in the parable of the loaves and fishes, there was always enough to feed the multitudes.

The residence auditorium comfortably accommodated numbers that first year, but the subsequent three years produced an ever increasing head count that eventually reached overflow proportions. In 1961, the banquet had to be moved to the Jubilee Auditorium to accommodate a flood of 600 attendees celebrating the association's Silver Anniversary. The auditorium provided the room, but not the atmosphere everyone had grown to love, nor the catering ease we'd grown to expect. After a second year at that location, we came back home... to a jam-packed auditorium. In the apparent absence of an alternative, the banquets were held in the residence for three years, before space was found at the Calgary Inn. The two years there, apparently with uncooperative management, were not happy ones, I'm told. There was a collective sigh of relief when the Palliser agreed to accommodate us once again. We have now been at the Palliser (in recent years, renamed the Fairmont Palliser) steadily since 1968, and any other venue would be unthinkable. In fact, we're quite certain we have squatters' rights.

For many years, I recall feeling sandwiched, even in the expanse of the Palliser's Crystal Room, but our present-day numbers have bought us more breathing space — a circumstance that is pleasing on the one hand, but disquieting on the other. Still, we turn up in stirring numbers at the Palliser on a Friday evening every May, as reliably as Mother's Day arrives on a Sunday. When the two occasions land on the same weekend, Mother's Day plays second fiddle. The hotel staff braces for a din of high-pitched shrieks in the lobby — standard accompaniment for the exchange of greetings and hugs. When we take our seats in the Crystal Room and they close the doors behind us, a muffled cacophony continues.

The original motivation for the banquets was to honor the new graduating class, but when the school closed, we did not break stride, We simply moved forward, celebrating one another at a "homecoming banquet." Individual classes take on the event's organizing assignment each year on a rotating basis, with each class's shift scheduled to not land on an anniversary year for that class. The tradition is that anniversaries are celebrated every five years. Each successive organizing committee is thunderstruck by the magnitude of the task, yet none have failed to surpass all expectations. Most of the women in attendance are celebrating a milestone anniversary, but a loyal few have attended every year since their graduation. One member of the Class of '59 has chalked up a perfect attendance record; another is able to claim an impressive 98%.

For some years, the highlight of the evening was a performance by *The Alumnae Players* — our own in-house drama society, headed by Eleanor Tregillus, with input from her husband Dick, a local radio announcer — the artistic couple of stained glass window fame. Their hilarious productions were so good that when they folded, no one had the courage to produce Act II. We have been blessed, however, with many talented soloists of every genre, who have contributed generously through the years to the enjoyment of the evening. And so it is that the entertainment has varied... but the rest of the evening has not.

The evening contains toasts, messages from absent sisters, and introductions of anniversary classes, as one would expect at any similar gathering, but it's our trademark traditions — those carved in stone — that we carry home in our hearts at day's end. For as far back as I can remember, we recited in unison a unique little poem written in 1953 by Vivian Katz (Florence '50) when she was press convener, to honor those who died during the previous year. It seemed to be absent from the last reunion I attended — for whatever reason — but as names of the deceased were read, the poem, "From our chain... " was running through my head:

> From our chain a link has fallen,
> In our land a star has set.
> But enshrined in Memory's Tablet
> Their true worth we'll ne'er forget.

In 1980, a new tradition was introduced, one designed to bestow guest-of-honor accolades to the class celebrating its fiftieth anniversary. Stalwarts of this group became affectionately known as "golden nuggets," a title intended to bring honor, but one that inevitably brings a disrespectful snicker. Each year, the class so honored elects a sister from its midst to present a review of their student days together. Edith Henry (Randall '30) led the way, delivering the first "golden nugget address." Since that night, everyone counts on surprises, tears and laughter as each new author reaches back through the years, but the invaluable bonus of the address is its historic recording of the times — a treasure to tuck into our archives.

As our evening comes to a close, the lights dim for our candle-lighting ceremony, symbolizing the passing of the flame from the lamp of Florence Nightingale, the first nurse, to those following her lead. Nightingale, the daughter of a wealthy landowner, was born in nineteenth century Italy, where she was given the name of her birthplace, Florence. She made a surprising decision to leave the comforts of the privileged to serve on the cholera-infested battlefront of Turkey. Those in her care reported the comfort she brought in the solitary darkness of long, frightening nights as she made rounds carrying her lamp. She became known as "The Lady with the Lamp." The lamp was later adopted by the nursing profession as its symbol.

Flora McInnes as Florence Nightingale

The role of Florence Nightingale is featured in the ceremony, and once again, the multitalented Eleanor Tregillus designed and fashioned a costume to fit our first lead, Flora McInnes, who carried the lamp with style from 1951 to 1985. When Flora retired from the role, her petite size ruled out most of us as viable understudies. Yet a willing *little* sister faithfully steps forward every year, and Florence lives on. In the original script of the ceremony, written by Tregillus, big sisters passed the flame to their little sisters in the graduating class, receiving them as full sisters of the profession. After the school closed, the ceremony was altered to signify a rededication of all graduates to the profession.

With candles aglow, we repeat the enduring *Florence Nightingale Pledge*:

> I solemnly pledge myself before God and in the presence of this assembly, to pass my life in purity and to practice my profession faithfully. I will abstain from whatever is deleterious and mischievous and will not take or knowingly administer any harmful drug. I will do all in my power to elevate the standards of my profession and will hold in confidence all personal matters committed to my keeping, and all family affairs coming to my knowledge in the practice of my calling. With loyalty, I endeavor to aid the physician in his work and devote myself to the welfare of those committed to my care.

The pledge, honoring the pioneer of modern nursing, was composed in 1893 by Lystra Gretter, an instructor of nursing at the old Harper Hospital in Detroit, Michigan. An adaptation of the *Hippocratic Oath* taken by doctors, it was first used by the Harper Hospital's spring graduating class of that year, and was eventually adopted by nursing classes at graduations across the continent.

The pledge found itself on shaky ground at the Calgary General Hospital, however, the year a student nurse was caught red handed in the medication room, dipping into supplies in direct contravention of the clause, "I will not take any harmful drug." A horrified Gertrude Hall suggested this unthinkable act negated her entire class from honorably taking a pledge that had already been broken. The alumnae stepped in with the argument that all nurses justified in taking the pledge must be allowed to do so. They added a further sentiment that the disgraced sister, now voicing repentance and a willingness to renew her promise, should be offered redemption. The alumnae won its case. Gertrude Hall introduced her independent thinking to another class.

The Class of '54 was in its senior year, and the Professional Adjustments class conducted by Miss Hall was a serious matter. When she put forward the idea of writing their own pledge for graduation, arguing it would have greater meaning if they wrote it themselves, they took up the challenge without hesitation. Drawing inspiration from the Code of Ethics adopted by the International Council of Nurses at its 1953 Quadrennial Congress in Brazil, they put their heads together, and came up with a Pledge they could call their own. On graduation day 1954, they recited it with great pride:

> I solemnly pledge myself before God and in the Presence of this assembly:
>
> To promote health, to alleviate suffering, and to conserve life, to the best of my ability.
>
> I will respect all religious beliefs, and care for all persons irrespective of color, race or creed.
>
> With loyalty, will I do all in my power to sustain confidence in the physician and to carry out faithfully and intelligently all orders given by him.
>
> I will participate and share responsibility with other citizens and health professions in promoting the health of all people.
>
> I pledge myself to maintain the highest standards of nursing care, and at all times will I strive to maintain the conduct of a truly professional nurse.

The departure from the Florence Nightingale Pledge ruffled a few feathers amongst the old guard who adhered to tradition. I don't know if future classes ever made a similar departure, but I do remember reciting the Florence Nightingale Pledge at my own graduation five years later, and noting the ire it raised with some of my sisters. Their stumbling block was the last line, beginning, "With loyalty, I endeavor to aid the physician in his work... " After three years of total dominance, they were finally winning independence, ready to advocate for themselves, and the line's suggestion of servitude to the doctor did not sit well. When I last repeated the same line at an Alumnae Homecoming Banquet, I did not see evidence of the same disdain. Perhaps with age and maturity, we have come to recognize the significance of a historic ritual.

Our evenings close with bowed heads for the Alumnae Prayer written by Eleanor Tregillus:

Calgary General Hospital Nurses' Alumnae Prayer

ur Father - give us grace today to think not of what we can get but of what we can give with a new vision and a new purpose. Grant to all nurses, wisdom and skill, diligence and patience.

Take away all hatred and prejudice and whatsoever else may hinder us from godly union and concord.

Guide our Alumnae Association and inspire each member to work willingly and whole-heartedly so that Thou wilt delight to bless our renewed spirit.

Amen.

Then we stampede out the Crystal Room doors and into the adjacent Oval Room for class photos. Lane's Studio has taken on this unimaginable assignment since time immemorial — the kind, jovial Roger Cyr positioning class after class of 50 plus women (author's intention is a reference to number, not age or size) in eye-pleasing rows, with those in the back row teetering treacherously on wobbly chairs. Throughout the positioning process, Mr. Cyr, with a glint in his eye, calmly and patiently juggles us into place as we banter non-stop. Mouths never stop moving even as he shifts shoulders and tilts heads to make us camera-ready. Then there's a moment of silence, Mr. Cyr gives us a wink, and — click! Two weeks later, a portrait of ageless beauties arrives in the mail, and we slip it into dog-eared albums of CGH collectibles at the back of our closets.

The Class of '59 — 30th Reunion — Palliser Hotel Oval Room

Photo: Lane's Studio, Calgary

It broke our hearts when Mr. Cyr retired in 1996. I'm told it broke his heart, too. "Roger absolutely lived for his annual date at the Palliser Hotel with the Calgary General ladies," said Andy Robichaud, his good-humored successor and former assistant. Then he added a touching note. Apparently, in his later years, Mr. Cyr never took a step without his cane, except for one day of the year. He left his cane in the car when he came into the Palliser Hotel in May, because he didn't want the nurses to be concerned. Mr. Cyr died in Saskatoon in 1998. Andy brings the very best of our beloved friend to our sittings now, and a new tradition with a new friend has been established. We're full of smiles.

Final Word

As I send this book to print, I'm faced with one last thought: *the countdown has begun... the merciless march toward the exalted state of nuggethood.* It's arrived faster than I could shake down a thermometer. I turned to my dictionary to see if becoming a nugget was as exalted as my alumnae would have me believe. The dictionary gave me this: nugget — a solid lump. *Well,* I thought, *if the shoe fits.* I reached for a second dictionary: nugget — a lump of native gold. *Better, but still a lump.* I tried the Web: nugget — anything valuable. *Aha, I'll run with this one!* And as I was running with it, I was suddenly struck with the revelation that the Class of '59 didn't have to wait fifty years to become nuggets; we've been nuggets all along. In fact, every sister, at every table, at every banquet, is a nugget — pure gold.

Gone are the iron lung, the oxygen tent, and the new-born nursery window where daddies and daughters held court through glass; gone are the morning bed bath, the nightly back rub, bibs and aprons... and gone is a master plan. But the Calgary General Hospital lives on: in the hearts of the long parade of Calgarians who gave — or received — tender loving care within its walls during its one-hundred-eight-year history; in the glistening eyes of a man at a farewell in June; in a brick propped against an office door... and in the enduring love of a steadfast sisterhood. It took twenty-three seconds for dynamite charges to blow in our walls; they did not blow out our lamp.

John Larter, Calgary Sun, October 1998 — with permission

– IN MEMORIAM –

Doug Byers
1961 - 2008

On March 4, 2008, I lost my beloved firstborn, Doug, age forty-six. He never left my thoughts as I worked through the final chapters of this book. Then, as I rolled out the last page, a long forgotten event came to mind: Doug was twenty-two years old; it was Halloween, 1983 — 6:00 p.m. The story went like this:

"Mom, I need a costume for the Halloween Party at SAIT tonight."

"Doug! This is a fine time to lay this on me. Do you think I'm some miracle worker?"

"Yup! You'll come up with something. You always do."

"In two hours?" I moan... to deaf ears. He's wolfing down his supper, serenely confident that a costume will appear like magic.

I head to the basement and begin rummaging through old clothes, hoping an idea will spring forth. In a bottom drawer, I discover my stash of CGH student uniforms. *Hm-m-m. Doug's trim physique will fit perfectly.*

"How would you like to be a nurse?" I ask, emerging from the depths bearing an armload of blue gingham and stiff white cotton.

"Perfect," he says, snatching up the dress and disappearing down the hall. I fumble with a cap I've forgotten how to fold, then turn to the finger-numbing task of pinning the bib to the apron.

Doug returns from the bedroom all "checked" out, the dress fitting beautifully just as I had surmised, with the exception of the sleeves that are binding the biceps. But he's not complaining. I button him into the bib and apron, pin on the cap, and step back to examine my inspired creation. He's maddeningly more beautiful in this outfit than I ever was. Then I reach for my lipstick to add the finishing touch.

"Doug," I say, as I begin daubing *Revlon apple polish* on his lips, "it's about your moustache — it's got to go."

"What do you mean it's got to go?" he replies, with a devilish smirk. "All nurses have moustaches."

My apologies to all sisters of the profession. Evidently, my son inherited his mother's black sense of humor.

Words cannot describe how much I miss my witty guy.

– ACKNOWLEDGEMENTS –

My grateful thanks to all my sisters who generously responded to my plea for stories and photos. I am particularly grateful for the steady flow of encouraging words that, without fail, accompanied their "assignment" submissions. Special thanks to Jean McLennan for her camera and companionship as we combed landmark sites together, and to Joy Whitehouse for entrusting me with her three irreplaceable scrapbooks for the past five years — an amazing chronicle of our student days together. And kudos to Sandra Handy, the glue that binds the Class of '59. Sam must have inherited the skills for keeping track of us from Mrs. Sanders, our beloved switchboard operator.

I am deeply touched by the charity of two treasured classmates — Catherine Heisen and Juline Hande — whose enthusiasm for the book never waned, even as they approached their final days. Cathy, from her deathbed in Portland, Oregon, arranged for the safe delivery of her invaluable scrapbook of photos and mementoes to my front door, through Pat Brearley, a Class of '59 sister, and Marianne Mundy, a Calgary niece. Cathy died November 23, 2006, two months after a final embrace with her Class of '59 sisters at Qualicum Beach, B.C. Julie's priceless, hand-written anecdotes regularly made their way to my mailbox from Esterhazy, Saskatchewan — rare treasures in a mailbox otherwise barren of such delights. Julie died May 16, 2008. Her last letter arrived two weeks prior.

Special thanks to "little sister" Catherine Smith (Munn '62) for her generosity in contributing the Foreword. And to "big sisters" Lois Wakefield (Class of '55), for *A Tribute to Our Hospital*; Alice Schwieger (Gehman '54) for a copy of her class's Graduation Pledge;

and Flora McInnes (McNeill '46) for willingly giving copious amounts of her time to answer my questions and accompany me on fact-finding missions and photo shoots. And to all alumnae sisters — the guardians of our lamp — who willingly delved into their memory banks to supply me with information.

I am indebted to the many people who picked up their telephone to an unfamiliar voice, or opened an e-mail from an unknown address, then went out of their way to answer questions posed by a stranger; every morsel of information they supplied was gladly received. Honorable mention goes to Colleen Roberts, Project Manager, *The Bridges* and Dennis Slater, Archivist/Curator of the Calgary Health Region collections. Preservation of our history is in good hands.

My untold gratitude for my editor, Rona Altrows, who assured me she could make my "magnum opus"☺ shine — and kept her word. Her passion as an editor was evident from the beginning; her compassion as a friend was an unforeseen bonus.

A huge thank you to Sherry Ward, my amazing layout and cover designer, for joining me in this, our second collaboration. Sherry has my deepest admiration for her brave undertaking of this assignment following a major setback from a stroke during surgery and resulting aphasia; her artistic genius has plainly pulled through unscathed.

Lastly, my eternal gratitude for my family — my husband, Dick, and our children, Diane and Stephen, and their precious families — whose healing embrace carried me through a year when our hearts were breaking. This book would not have made it to the finish line without their love and support.

236

- BIBLIOGRAPHY -

Bobrovitz, Jennifer, *Cornerstones, The Calgary Herald*, June 7, 1998.

Boschma, Geertje, *Faculty of Nursing on the Move: Nursing at the University of Calgary, 1969-2004*, University of Calgary Press, 2006.

Bowness Historical Society, editor Carpenter, Carole, *Bowness: Our Village in the Valley*, 2005.

Calgary General Hospital, *Centres of Excellence*, Commemorative Issue, 1988.

Canadian Nurses' Association, *Spotlight on Nursing Education: The Report of the Pilot Project for the Evaluation of Schools of Nursing in Canada* — Director: Helen K. Mussallem, Ottawa, 1960.

Editorial Committee, *Calgary General Hospital 1890-1955, Sixty-five Years of Community Service*.

Eisler, Dale, *An Unprecedented Hospital Closing in Calgary, Maclean's, April 28, 1997*.

Hankins, Gerald W., *Rolling On, The Story of the Amazing Gary McPherson*, The University of Alberta Press, 2003.

Henry, Edith A. (Randall '30) & McIntyre, E. Jean (Moon '31), *25 Years of Alumnae Life, 1936-1961*.

Mussallem, Helen K., *Nursing Education in Canada, Royal Commission On Health Services*, Queen's Printer, Ottawa, 1965.

Richardson, Sharon L., *Stand Up and Be Counted, Nursing at the Calgary General Hospital after the Second World War*.

Ross-Kerr, Janet C., *Prepared to Care, Nurses and Nursing in Alberta*, The University of Alberta Press, 1998.

Scollard, D., *Hospital, A Portrait of Calgary General*, Calgary General Hospital, 1981.

Also by Eleanor King Byers

The House With The Light On

— a native Calgarian returns to the forties and fifties —
days of unlocked doors and carefree adventure.

Eleanor King Byers draws a portrait of Calgary during its safer, gentler
days in this light-hearted memoir of her childhood and youth in the 1940s
and '50s. Visit all her favorite haunts — schools, church, playgrounds,
sports arenas and movie theatres — hunt porcupines in the coulee, bury
your shoes in William Roper Hull's garden, and sip tea at the Tea Kettle
Inn, her family's noted restaurant of the time.

Praise for The House With The Light On

"... a warm and funny family history. Eleanor King Byers proves
scandal isn't necessary to liven up one's memoirs. With a keen eye
for relevant detail, she has captured the essence of growing up in
Calgary in the 1940s and '50s."

David Bly, The Calgary Herald

"If you lived in Calgary then, you will love this book. If you are new
to Calgary or somewhat younger, you will enjoy Eleanor's guided
tour of what will often feel like another world."

Ruben Nelson, Lac Des Arcs, AB

"Thank you for writing the history of the Calgary we grew up in
and making it live so tangibly once again."

Allan Sheftel, Vancouver, B.C.

History/Memoir/0-9733420-0-5